THE

INTERNATIONAL SERIES

OF

MONOGRAPHS ON PHYSICS

GENERAL EDITORS

R. H. FOWLER AND P. KAPITZA

ECLIPSES

OF THE

SUN AND MOON

BY

Sir FRANK DYSON, K.B.E., F.R.S.

LATE ASTRONOMER ROYAL

AND

R. v. d. R. WOOLLEY, Ph.D.

CHIEF ASSISTANT AT THE ROYAL OBSERVATORY
GREENWICH

OXFORD

AT THE CLARENDON PRESS

1937

OXFORD UNIVERSITY PRESS

AMEN HOUSE, E.C. 4

LONDON EDINBURGH GLASGOW NEW YORK

TORONTO MELBOURNE CAPETOWN BOMBAY

CALCUTTA MADRAS

HUMPHREY MILFORD

PUBLISHER TO THE UNIVERSITY

Collated.

A.

B.

PRINTED IN GREAT BRITAIN

PREFACE

THE authors of this book are conscious that the treatment of many of the subjects touched upon has been extremely brief. Nevertheless, it is their hope that few points of importance have not been mentioned and that few observational results have not been enumerated, so that the reader will be given a comprehensive survey of the subject. In the chapters of astrophysical interest we have not described the apparatus in detail, nor have we ventured far into physical theory, but we have endeavoured to present an accurate description of the actual observations and of the deductions which may immediately be made from them.

We are indebted to Professor W. W. Campbell and to M. Lyot who have kindly sent us photographs which we have reproduced in this book. M. Lyot has also given permission to use certain unpublished measures.

It is a pleasure to record our grateful thanks to Professor R. H. Fowler for the care with which he has edited the book, to Professor W. H. McCrea who has read the chapter on the Equilibrium of the Chromosphere in both manuscript and proof and offered constructive suggestions at both stages, and to Mr. C. R. Davidson who has read through the whole of the manuscript and assisted us with the chapter on the Deflexion of Light by the Sun's Gravitational Field.

F. W. D.
R. v. d. R. W.

CONTENTS

I. INTRODUCTION 1

> The General Appearance of a Total Eclipse of the Sun. The Cause of Eclipses. Their Importance in Astronomy. The Total Eclipse's Importance in Astrophysics. Lunar Eclipses.

II. CAUSE OF ECLIPSES 4

> Ecliptic Limits. The Number of Eclipses that can occur in a Year. Total and Annular Eclipses. Canon der Finsternisse.

III. THE PREDICTION OF ECLIPSES 11

> Prediction of a Lunar Eclipse. The Prediction of Solar Eclipses. The Besselian Elements of the Eclipse. The Coordinates on the Fundamental Plane of a Point on the Earth's Surface. Calculation of the Beginning and End of an Eclipse. Numerical Example. Centre of Track of Total Eclipse. Duration of Eclipse at Centre and Size of Shadow.

IV. THE SAROS 24

> Metonic Cycle.

V. ECLIPSES OF THE MOON 29

> Lunar Eclipses in Antiquity; The Shape of the Earth. Colour of the Moon during an Eclipse. Spectrum of Eclipsed Moon. Occultations. Observations of Temperature.

VI. THE SECULAR ACCELERATION 36

> Discovery by Halley. Dunthorne's Determination of Amount. Laplace's Explanation. Correction by Adams. Secular Variation of the Sun's Longitude. Fotheringham's Investigation. Tidal Friction in the Irish Sea.

VII. THE DEFLEXION OF LIGHT BY THE SUN'S GRAVITATIONAL FIELD 43

> British Expeditions. Rediscussion of the Observations. Lick Observatory Expedition. Freundlich's Expedition.

VIII. ECLIPSES IN RELATION TO THE PHYSICAL STATE OF THE SUN FROM 1836 TO 1889 51

> Early Visual Observations. Corona and Prominences. The First Photographic and Spectroscopic Observations. Observations from 1870 to 1875. Observations from 1878 to 1889.

IX. ECLIPSE EXPEDITIONS—INSTRUMENTS . . 57

> Fall of Illumination and Temperature. Diminishing Crescent. Schaberle's Fixed Telescope. Campbell's Polar Axis. The Coelostat.

X. THE FLASH SPECTRUM 64

The Solar Spectrum at Second Contact. Enhanced Lines in the Chromosphere. Observations of the Chromospheric Spectrum without Eclipse. The Theoretical Problem presented by the Enhanced Lines. Ionization. Recent Chromospheric Spectra. Description of the Flash Spectrum.

XI. LINE INTENSITY IN THE CHROMOSPHERIC SPECTRUM   75

Direct Observations of Intensity in the Spectrum of the Chromosphere. Observations of Intensity in the Flash Spectrum in 1927. The Balmer Decrement in the Prominences in 1927. Observations of the Balmer Decrement without Eclipse. The Relative Abundance of the Elements and their Distribution with Height in the Chromosphere. The Density Gradient of the Chromosphere.

XII. THE EQUILIBRIUM OF THE CHROMOSPHERE   . 89

The Theory of Selective Radiation Pressure. The Special Case of Complete Support. Chandrasekhar's Theory of the Dynamics of the Chromosphere. Transfer of Momentum from Ca^+ to other Elements; Viscosity. Turbulence. Support by Momentum derived from Coronal Streamers.

XIII. PHOTOGRAPHY OF THE CORONA. THE SOLAR CYCLE   103

Coronal Arches. Changes in Corona. Photography of the Corona without an Eclipse.

XIV. INTENSITY OF CORONAL LIGHT. TOTAL LIGHT   . 111

Total Light of the Corona. Bolometric Observations. Surface Brightness of the Corona.

XV. POLARIZATION OF THE CORONA   .   .   . 126

Theory of Polarization of the Corona developed by Schuster. Comparison of Schuster's Formulae with Observation made by Young. Observations by Dufay and Grouiller, 1932. Visual Observations by Johnson, 1934. Atmospheric Polarization. Recent Observations.

XVI. THE SPECTRUM OF THE CORONA   .   .   . 134

Absorption Lines. Continuous Spectrum. Bright Lines in the Spectrum of the Corona. Intensities of the Emission Lines of the Corona. Spectrum of Corona obtained without an Eclipse. Coronal Lines in RS Ophiuchi.

XVII. THE NATURE OF THE CORONA   .   .   . 152

Early Theories of the Nature of the Corona. The Corona considered as composed of Particles of Atomic Dimensions. The Corona Particles considered as Dust Particles.

INDEX OF NAMES. 159

LIST OF ILLUSTRATIONS

Successive Phases of a Total Eclipse of the Sun . . *Frontispiece*

PLATE I. A Description of the Passage of the Shadow of the Moon over England . . . . *facing p.* 9

„ II. Restricted Equatorial Mounting as used by Campbell in 1922 . . . . „ 61

„ III. Coelostat and Long-Focus Camera (Pacific and Atlantic Photos., Ltd.) . . . „ 63

„ IV. Flash Spectrum, 1898 (Fowler) . . . „ 65

„ V. (*a*) Ultra-Violet Spectrum of Chromosphere (Slit Spectroscope). (*b*) Spectrum of Chromosphere (Objective Prism) . . . . „ 71

„ VI. Moving-Plate Photograph showing Spectrum of the Sun near its Limb. The upper photo shows a part enlarged about 3½ times (Campbell) . „ 72

„ VII. (*a*) Corona 1900. Minimum Phase. (*b*) Corona, 1898. Intermediate Phase . . *between pp.* 104, 105

„ VIII. (*a*) Corona, 1927. Maximum Phase. (*b*) Corona, 1927. Maximum Phase . . . „ „

„ IX. (*a*) Stereoscopic Photograph showing the Diffused Light of a Simple Lens (Lyot). (*b*) Corona of 1936 July 7 (Lyot) . . . . *facing p.* 109

„ X. (*a*) Spectrum of Corona, 1905. (*b*) Ultra-Violet Spectrum of Corona, 1926 . . . „ 143

„ XI. Spectroheliogram of the Corona of 1931 Aug. 7 in the light of 5,303 A. (Lyot) . . . „ 146

I

INTRODUCTION

The General Appearance of a Total Eclipse of the Sun. The gradual darkening of the Sun in full daylight, culminating in its complete obscuration for a few minutes, followed by an equally slow return to complete brightness has in previous ages brought alarm and apprehension. Among savage tribes the beating of tom-toms and other incantations are still used to propitiate the dragon which is supposed to devour the Sun. Even now in India, where eclipses are predicted in the local press, ancient ceremonies are still carried through as a matter of ritual. It is no wonder that animals are disturbed, and that birds sometimes go to roost. Though the cause is completely understood, a total eclipse of the Sun is a most impressive and awe-inspiring spectacle to every intelligent beholder.

For a short time after the commencement of an eclipse no appreciable diminution of light is noticed, but an observer provided with darkened glasses sees a black sector on the west side of the Sun. This gradually increases for about an hour and a half. The temperature falls a few degrees and a slight change in the colour of the light gives a weird aspect to the landscape. The total obscuration arrives very suddenly, bringing with it a dramatic change. Red flames called prominences are seen proceeding from the darkened disk. A white aureole called the Corona encircles the disk with streamers stretching in some directions to several degrees. Some of the brighter stars and the planets Mercury and Venus appear in the sky which is now as bright as at twilight. The spectacle lasts but a few minutes and ends as suddenly as it began. A bright crescent appears on the west of the Sun, which increases till the eclipse is over in another hour and a half. The Frontispiece shows the sequence of the phases of an eclipse.

The rarity of the occurrence of a total eclipse at any point on the Earth's surface accounts in no small measure for the interest it arouses. Most people never see one in the course of their lives. In London no total eclipse was visible in the nineteenth century or will be in the twentieth.

Partial eclipses are of much more frequent occurrence, but are of a much less striking character. The light of the Sun is, roughly speaking, 500,000 times as great as that of the Moon, which is comparable with the light of the Corona. If half the Sun's light is cut off, the difference is hardly noticed, and is not nearly so great as that produced by a cloudy sky. Even when the eclipse is annular, and at its central phase only a bright rim is seen, the light may well be 1/100th part of the total sunlight, or 5,000 times that of the full Moon, and quite sufficient to hide both the Corona and prominences.

The Cause of Eclipses. Their Importance in Astronomy. The cause of eclipses of the Sun is that the Moon in its monthly orbit round the Earth is sometimes in the direct line between these two bodies. It happens that the Moon as seen from the Earth has an apparent diameter nearly equal to that of the Sun. Owing mainly to the variation in distance of the Moon from the Earth, its apparent diameter is sometimes greater, sometimes smaller than that of the Sun. In the first case the eclipse is total, in the second annular. This seemingly trivial circumstance of the near equality of the diameters of Sun and Moon as seen from the Earth gives rise to the most interesting phenomena of eclipses. Had the Moon's diameter been 2,000 miles instead of 2,160, neither prominences nor Corona would have been seen, and we should have known little of the Sun's atmosphere and its immediate surroundings.

Astronomers were attracted to the study of eclipses in the first instance for the purpose of their accurate prediction. After the publication of the *Principia*, the value of eclipses was mainly regarded as affording information on the movement of the Moon. By comparison of records of times and places of historic eclipses, Halley discovered a gradual but very slow shortening of the month, which has ultimately been traced to a lengthening of the day due to the friction of the tides.

The Total Eclipse's Importance in Astrophysics. About a hundred years ago the sight of the red flames created an enthusiasm among astronomers which still persists and leads them to distant parts of the Earth. In 1868 the red flames were found to be due to hydrogen, and a method was devised of seeing them in full sunlight. Two years later a sudden change from a dark line to a bright line spectrum was discovered by spectroscopic observations at the instant the eclipse became total. This was at first regarded as the 'reversing layer' which caused the dark lines in the solar spectrum. Further investigation revealed important differences between the character of the solar spectrum and that which is now known as the chromo-spheric spectrum. Many lines were found to be enhanced, i.e. their intensity was found to correspond with the higher temperature of the electric spark than the arc. Later it was found that these par-ticular lines came from ionized elements, and the difficulty was finally resolved by consideration of conditions of pressure and tem-perature at the Sun's surface. Meanwhile the spectrum of the Corona was found to give a continuous spectrum with a few bright lines of unknown origin reaching to a few minutes of arc from the Sun's limb, and at greater distances to show a few of the stronger Fraunhofer lines. Polariscopic observations indicated a radial polari-zation of the Coronal light, showing that its light was, in part, sunlight scattered by small particles.

Visual observations have been largely replaced by photographs in recent years. Direct photographs of the form of the Corona have confirmed its variation of form in the solar cycle indicated by spots and prominences. Photographs of the spectrum of the chromosphere have been responsible for establishing differences between the chromo-spheric spectrum and that of the normal solar surface. The Corona spectrum has been shown to agree in colour with that of the Sun, a result confirmed generally by bolometric observations.

Total eclipses have also made it possible to photograph the field of stars surrounding the Sun and thus to verify the prediction from the generalized theory of relativity of the deflexion of light by the Sun's gravitational field.

Lunar Eclipses. Lunar eclipses have only a minor interest and importance. The spectacle is, however, one of great beauty, though it has not the impressiveness of a total solar eclipse. Before the eclipse, with the Moon at full, only the brightest stars are seen. As the eclipse proceeds, more stars become visible, till at the total phase, which may last for hours, the sky is filled with stars. Lunar eclipses have an historic importance for their clear demonstration of the rotundity of the Earth. They provided, too, the means of an accurate determination of the Moon's distance, and thus established the much greater distance of the Sun and planets. In recent times the measurement of the rapid change of temperature of the Moon as it comes into the shadow have led to interesting speculations on the nature of the Moon's surface.

II

CAUSE OF ECLIPSES

ECLIPSES occur when the Sun, Earth, and Moon are in the same straight line or nearly so. If the Moon lies between the Earth and the Sun, over some part of the Earth a segment of the Sun's disk is hidden by the Moon. If, on the contrary, the Earth lies between the Sun and Moon, the shadow of the Earth cast by the Sun covers a portion or the whole of the Moon. If the Moon moved round the Earth in the ecliptic or plane in which the Earth moves round the Sun, eclipses both solar and lunar would occur every month. But the plane of the Moon's orbit is inclined at 5° 8' to the ecliptic, so that eclipses can only occur when the alinement of the three bodies takes place in their orbits near the line of intersection of the two orbital planes. If we think of these planes as circles on the celestial sphere, the points of intersection are the nodes of the lunar orbit, ascending when the Moon's orbit crosses the ecliptic from south to north and descending in the converse case.

The conditions under which eclipses can occur are readily seen from the diagram. The Sun and Earth are spheres whose centres are at S and E. Enveloping these spheres are two cones, the exterior one with vertex at V and the interior one with vertex at U. The Moon is shown in several positions, K, L, K', L'.

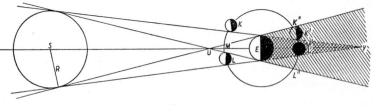

FIG. 1

If the Moon is at K it will just avoid obscuration of any part of the Sun's light on the Earth. If, however, it falls inside the cone, there will be a total eclipse at some part of the Earth. In all intermediate positions a partial eclipse of the Sun will occur.

When the Moon is in opposition, it may fall completely inside the shadow or *Umbra* of the Earth as at L'. In this case it will be seen totally eclipsed from all parts of the Earth turned towards it. If, however, it is at K', it will just avoid being in the full shadow. But between the limits K'' and L'' part of the Sun's light will be cut off in amount increasing to its proximity to the complete shadow. In this case the eclipse is *Penumbral.*

We will examine in the first place the conditions under which an eclipse will occur when the Sun and Moon are at their mean distances from the Earth.

Let R be the radius of the Sun, equal to 432,050 miles,

,,	r	,,	,,	Earth, ,,	3,959 ,,
,,	ρ	,,	,,	Moon, ,,	1,080 ,,

Let D be the mean distance of the Sun from the Earth, equal to 92,870,000 miles.

Let d be the mean distance of the Moon from the Earth, equal to 238,900 miles.

Let θ be the semi-vertical angle of the cone at the vertex (V in Fig. 1).

Then $\sin \theta = (R-r)/D$, so that $\theta = 15' \ 51''$.

The distance of the centre of the Earth from the vertex, EV, is 859,000 miles.

The distance of the centre of the Moon at conjunction from the vertex, MV is 1,097,900 miles.

The distance of the centre of the Moon at opposition from the vertex, $M'V$ is 620,100 miles.

The radii of the sections of the cone at M and M' are 5,062 miles and 2,859 miles respectively. Inspection of the figure shows us that a partial eclipse of the Sun will occur at conjunction if the centre of the Moon is nearer to M than the position K, where $KM = 5,062+1,080 = 6,142$ miles, subtending an angle of $88 \cdot 3'$ at the Earth's centre: that is, if the geocentric position of the Moon differs by less than $88 \cdot 3'$ from that of the Sun.

Again, a total eclipse of the Sun will occur if the Moon is nearer to M than L, where $ML = 5,062-1,080 = 3,982$ miles, subtending $57 \cdot 3'$ at the Earth's centre, that is, if the geocentric position of the Moon differs by less than $57 \cdot 3'$ from that of the Sun.

Again $K'M' = 2,859+1,080 = 3,939$ miles, subtending an angle of $56 \cdot 7'$ at the Earth's surface, and $L'M' = 2,859-1,080 = 1,779$ miles, subtending $25 \cdot 6'$. Accordingly a total eclipse of the Moon will occur at opposition if the position of the centre of the Moon differs by less than $25 \cdot 6'$ from the position opposite to that of the Sun. In a similar manner it can be shown that there will be a penumbral eclipse if the centre of the Moon comes within 115′ of the position opposite to that of the centre of the Sun.

These limiting values apply only when the Sun and Moon are at their mean distances from the Earth, and the true values depend on the varying Moon's distance and to a lesser degree on the varying distance of the Sun.

Ecliptic Limits. The Moon touches the cone circumscribing the

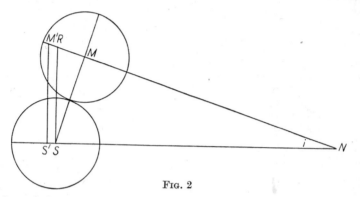

Fɪɢ. 2

Earth and Sun very near the time of its conjunction in longitude with the Sun. In Fig. 2 N is the node of the Moon's orbit, S and M the centres of the Sun and Moon when their angular distance apart is least, S' and M' at their conjunction in longitude. As the motion of the Moon in longitude is 13 times that of the Sun, we may take $S'M'$ as equal to $SR = SM \sec i$, where i is the inclination of the Moon's orbit and has the mean value 5° 8′. The longitude of the node is then obtained from the formula

$$\sin \lambda = \tan b \cot i,$$

where b stands for $S'M'$, the latitude of the Moon at opposition.

In the four cases considered above $S'M'$ is 88·7′, 57·5′, 56·9′, and 25·7′, and the corresponding values of λ are 16·6°, 10·8°, 10·5°, and 4·8°.

These are known as the ecliptic limits for *mean* values of the Moon's distance, Sun's distance, and inclination of the ecliptic. They vary considerably from eclipse to eclipse principally on account of the change in the distance of the Moon, and to a less extent to a change in the Sun's distance and the inclination of the Moon's orbit.

A partial eclipse is possible when the conjunction of the Sun and

Moon in longitude is as far from the node as 18° 31', and is certain to occur when it is less than 15° 21' from the node. A lunar eclipse is possible when the Moon in opposition is 12° 15' from the node, and must occur when it is less than 9° 30'.

The Number of Eclipses that can occur in a Year. Although of little importance, it is a matter of curious interest to find the maximum and minimum number of eclipses that can occur in a year. This is readily inferred from the ecliptic limits just given. The Sun moves nearly 1° a day, and consequently will move a smaller distance than the interval from −18° 31' to +18° 31' in a month. It is therefore possible to have a solar eclipse at two successive new Moons and a lunar eclipse between them. A lunar eclipse at successive full Moons is not possible.

The Moon's nodes regress on the ecliptic in a little under 19 years, or approximately 20 days a year. Ascending and descending nodes follow alternately after 173 days. The synodical month—i.e. the mean interval from new Moon to new Moon—is 29·5 days. The interval between the nodes is therefore 4 days less than six lunations. It is possible for three nodes to occur in the same year with a margin of 19 days distributed between the beginning of January and the end of December. If an eclipse of the Moon fell 4 days before the node in January, it will fall on the node near the end of June, and 4 days after the node in December. There may thus be three eclipses of the Moon and four of the Sun in the year, one after the lunar eclipse in January, two including the lunar eclipse in the middle of the year, and one preceding the lunar eclipse in December.

It is also possible for two eclipses of the Sun and one of the Moon to occur at successive nodes, and a fifth eclipse of the Sun to precede the node in December. As the first lunar eclipse of the year could not have been earlier than January 15, the one following the December node being 354 days later will be thrown into the next year.

Thus it is possible to have in one year

> 4 eclipses of the Sun and 3 of the Moon (partial, total or annular),

or   5 eclipses of the Sun and 2 of the Moon (partial or total).

A solar eclipse must occur near each node but a lunar eclipse need not necessarily do so.

The minimum number of eclipses in a year is therefore two and both are solar.

Total and Annular Eclipses. When the Moon lies directly between some point of the Earth's surface and the Sun, the eclipse may be total—i.e. the Moon may completely obscure the Sun, or it may be annular, i.e. the Moon will be enclosed in the Sun's disk and a bright annulus will surround the dark Moon.

If the vertex of the conical shadow of the Moon falls inside the

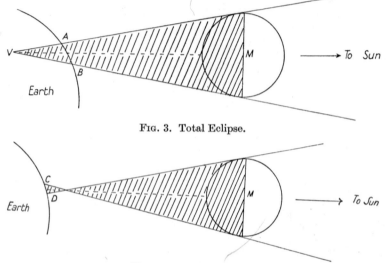

FIG. 3. Total Eclipse.

FIG. 4. Annular Eclipse.

Earth, then at any point within AB of Fig. 3 the Sun will be completely obscured.

In the second diagram, at any point in CD a bright annulus of the Sun will enclose the dark Moon.

If ρ be the radius of the Moon and R that of the Sun, $MV = \dfrac{\rho}{R-\rho} D$, where D is the distance of the Sun and Moon.

$\rho = 1,080$ miles, $R = 432,000$ miles. Thus $MV = D/399$.

The mean distance of the Moon from the Sun when it lies between the Sun and Earth is 92,630,000 miles, varying 1/60th part either way on account of the eccentricity of the Earth's orbit. $MV = 232,000 \pm 4,000$ miles. The mean distance of the Moon from the Earth's centre is 239,000 miles, or about 235,000 miles from the point on the Earth's surface nearest the Moon. Thus V will sometimes be between the Earth and the Moon, and sometimes inside the Earth or even beyond it.

PLATE 1

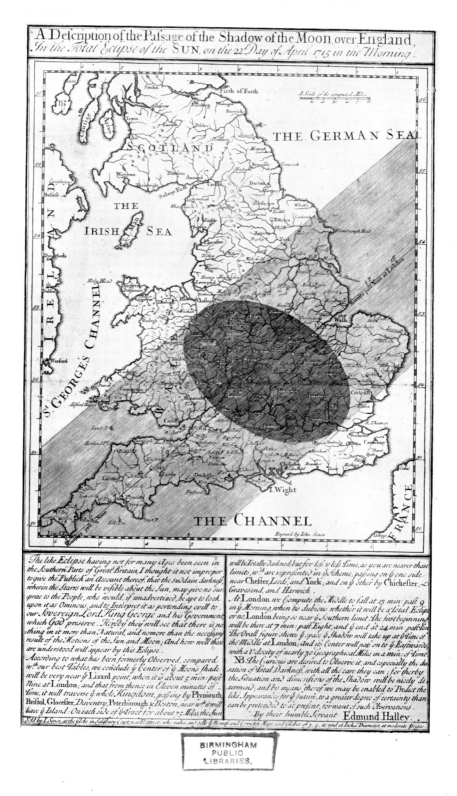

A Description of the Passage of the Shadow of the Moon over England, In the Total Eclipse of the SUN, on the 22d Day of April 1715 in the Morning.

The minimum distance of the Moon from the Earth's centre is 221,700 miles. If the direction of the axis of the shadow is normal to the Earth's surface, the place where the shadow falls is 217,700 miles from the Moon. The largest value of MV is 236,000 miles and thus V is 18,300 miles behind this place. The angle of the cone is 31′ 28″ and the breadth of the shadow is 167 miles. The breadth of the shadow cannot exceed this amount, but the length will be greater when the projection is oblique.

In the other extreme case the vertex of the shadow may fall as much as 20,300 miles short of the Earth's surface. The angle of the cone is 32′32″ and at normal incidence gives a breadth of 192 miles.

The angle which the breadth of the shadow subtends at the Moon is a measure of the excess of the Moon's diameter over that of the Sun at the place of observation. For the maximum shadow of 167 miles, this amounts to 2′ 38″. Similarly, for a maximum annular eclipse the Moon's apparent diameter is less than that of the Sun by 2′ 40″.

Plate 1 shows the position of the shadow at the eclipse of April 22, 1715, at 13ᵐ after noon at London. The breadth of the shadow is about 100 miles. Figures on the central line indicate the times at which the eclipse was central at these places. Thus the shadow was travelling over the Earth at a rate of nearly 30 miles a minute.

Canon der Finsternisse. Oppolzer[†] has given very complete tables from which the elements of all eclipses from −1207 November 10 (Julian Calendar) to 2161 November 17 (Gregorian Calendar) may be calculated. These include 8,000 eclipses of the Sun and 5,200 of the Moon. They are accompanied by maps showing the tracks of the central line for all total or annular solar eclipses which are north of latitude −30°. These tracks are drawn through three calculated places when the eclipse is total or annular at sunrise, midday, or sunset. The tracks are correct on the scale of the maps for modern eclipses, but for ancient eclipses may be a few degrees in error. They were calculated from Hansen's tables of the Moon and Leverrier's of the Sun, based on Oppolzer's[‡] 'Tables of Syzygies of the Moon'. Ginzel,[||] from the study of ancient eclipses, found empirical corrections to Oppolzer's tables of syzygies which were employed by

† *Canon der Finsternisse* (Vienna, 1887).
‡ 'Syzygientafeln für den Mond', *Astr. Ges.* **16** (1881).
|| *Astronomische Untersuchungen über Finsternisse.* (Acad. of Vienna, 1883–4.)

Schram† to give corrections to Oppolzer's *Canon der Finsternisse*. The whole subject was reviewed later by Schoch,‡ who used Newcomb's tables of the Sun and Brown's of the Moon, and gives for the Sun a secular term $+2 \cdot 5''\ T^2$, and for the Moon $+12 \cdot 0''\ T^2$.

From Oppolzer's canon the average number of eclipses of the Sun in 100 years is found to be 238. Of these

84 are partial,
66 are total,
77 are annular,
11 are partly annular and partly total.

The average number of lunar eclipses in 100 years is 154, of which 71 are total.

These figures are in fair accordance with what would be expected from the ecliptic limits.

† *Vienna K. Akad. Denk.* Band **56** (1889).
‡ *Neubearbeitung der Syzygientafeln von Oppolzer*, Rechen-Institut, Berlin-Dahlem. Band **2**, No. 2 (1928).

THE PREDICTION OF ECLIPSES

Prediction of a Lunar Eclipse. The prediction of the time of a lunar eclipse is a comparatively simple matter, and a graphic solution correct to within a few minutes is readily obtained from the data in the *Nautical Almanac*. It is convenient to use parallaxes and angular

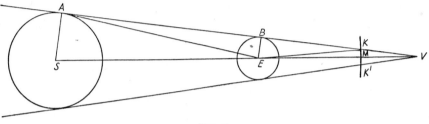

Fig. 5

diameters rather than distances and diameters in miles or kilometres, as these are the quantities which are tabulated.

Let S be the centre of the Sun,

E the centre of the Earth,

V the vertex of the enveloping cone,

KMK' the section of the shadow at the Moon's distance,

A, B the points of contact of the cone with Sun and Earth.

The angle KEM is one-half the angle which the umbral shadow subtends at the centre of the Earth.

$$KEM = BKE - BVE,$$

also

$$BVE = AES - BAE,$$

so that

$$KEM = BKE - AES + BAE.$$

But BKE is the angle the Earth's radius subtends at the Moon; i.e. the parallax of the Moon, or π'.

AES is the semi-diameter of the Sun as seen from the centre of the Earth, or s.

BAE is the angle subtended by a radius of the Earth at the distance of the Sun; i.e. the Sun's parallax, or π.

We have accordingly that the angular diameter of the umbral shadow at the distance of the Moon equals $\pi' - s + \pi$.

Similarly, the angular diameter of the penumbral shadow equals $\pi'+s+\pi$.

It is necessary to find the times when the Moon, whose semi-diameter is s', enters and leaves the shadow, the position angles of the points of contact with the shadow, and the course of the centre of the Moon through the shadow.

Running through the *Nautical Almanac* it is easy to see when the Moon is full near one of its nodes. For example, in 1931 on April 3·0 the Moon's age is 14·7^d when its latitude is $-1'$; and on September 27·0 its age is 14·8^d when its latitude is $-3'$.

On Apr. 3·0^d Moon's long. $= 194°\ 33'\ 58''$, Sun's long. $=\ \ 12°\ 16'\ 54''$
,, Sept. 27·0^d　　,,　　　,,　$=\ \ \ 4°\ 50'\ 19''$, ,,　　,,　$= 182°\ 55'\ \ 8''$
Hence, the difference between the longitude of the centre of the shadow and that of the Sun is $2°\ 17'\ 4''$ and $1°\ 55'\ 11''$ respectively. Thus an eclipse of the Moon falls near each of these dates.

It is now convenient to turn to right ascension and declination as the Moon's right ascension and declination are calculated for each hour in the Almanac, and the Sun's right ascension and declination are readily found by interpolation. The Sun's and Moon's apparent right ascension and declination taken from the *Nautical Almanac* for Universal Time, U.T., (reckoned from midnight at Greenwich) for the four times April 2^d 18^h, 2^d 20^h, 2^d 22^h, 3^d 0^h are as follows:

U.T.	⊙'s App. R.A.	☽'s App. R.A.	Diff.	In arc.
d. h.	h. m. s.	h. m. s.	m. s.	′
Apr. 2 18	0 44 15·26	12 40 14·66	−4 0·60	−60·2
20	44 33·47	44 41·63	+8·16	+2·0
22	44 51·68	49 8·84	+4 17·16	+64·3
Apr. 3 0	45 9·89	53 36·31	+8 26·42	..

U.T.	⊙'s App. Dec.	☽'s App. Dec.	Diff.	In arc.
d. h.	° ′ ″	° ′ ″	′ ″	′
Apr. 2 18	+4 45 31·2	−3 58 29·0	+47 2·2	+47·0
20	47 26·6	−4 34 20·3	+13 6·3	+13·1
22	49 22·0	−5 10 3·7	−20 41·7	−20·7
Apr. 3 0	51 17·4	−5 45 38·3	−65 39·1	..

The differences are taken in the sense, Moon—Point opposite the Sun.

The Moon's horizontal parallax on April 2^d 20^h is 61′ 3·2″ and its semi-diameter 16′ 38·1″. The Sun's semi-diameter is 16′ 1·4″ and its parallax 8·8″. The semi-diameter of the shadow (umbra) is therefore

$$61'\ 3·2''+8·8''-16'\ 1·4'' = 45'\ 10·6''\ \text{or}\ 45·2'.$$

The graphical determination of the points of contact is made by plotting in rectangular coordinates the differences of right ascension and declination between the Moon and a point opposite the Sun Since the declination is small it is a good rough approximation to project the celestial sphere on to the tangent plane in this simple way; the scale of one degree of declination on the paper must be set equal to the scale of one degree of right ascension multiplied by the cosine of the mean declination. The cone of the umbra and

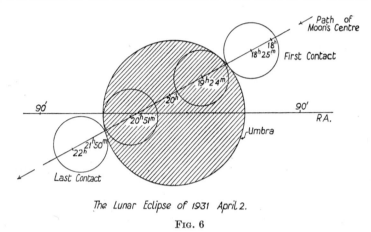

The Lunar Eclipse of 1931 April 2.

FIG. 6

the outline of the Moon are represented by small circles on the celestial sphere and approximately by circles on the tangent plane. Fig. 6 shows the representation of the eclipse of 1931 April 2. The umbra is represented by a circle centred at the origin with a radius equal to 45·2′. The path of the Moon's centre is found by plotting its position at 18^h, 20^h, and 22^h, and joining these points by a straight line. Contacts are found by drawing circles of radius 16·6′ to touch the umbra. The times of contact are found by linear interpolation between 18^h and 22^h, and are shown in the figure. The eclipse is central at $19^h 55^m$ U.T.; the sidereal time at Greenwich is $8^h 35^m$, and as the Moon's apparent right ascension is $12^h 45^m$ the eclipse will be central on the meridian in terrestrial longitude 62° 30′ E. of Greenwich.

The Prediction of Solar Eclipses. The appearance of a solar eclipse varies from one part of the Earth's surface to another, in contrast to the lunar eclipse which is the same at all places; hence the prediction of the circumstances of a solar eclipse at any place is a more complicated matter than that of a lunar eclipse. The method of prediction generally adopted for a solar eclipse is due to Bessel. This method depends on the use of a fundamental plane defined as a plane passing through the Earth's centre and perpendicular to the line joining the centres of the Sun and the Moon. Rectangular coordinates are chosen such that the origin is the centre of the Earth and the z-axis is parallel to the line SM joining the Sun and the Moon, so that the xy plane is the fundamental plane. The (positive) axis of x passes through the (eastward) intersection of the equator and the fundamental plane (Fig. 7). It is clear that the yz plane contains the Earth's pole.

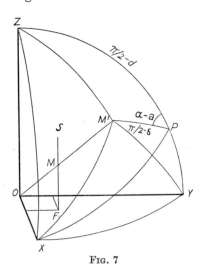

Fig. 7

Let α, δ, π, r, be the right ascension, declination, parallax, and distance from the centre of the Earth of the Moon, and let $\alpha', \delta', \pi', r'$, be the corresponding quantities for the Sun, and a, d the right ascension and declination of the line joining the centres of the Sun and Moon. The coordinates of the centres of the Moon and Sun are as follows:

Moon
$$x = r\cos\delta\sin(\alpha-a)$$
$$y = r\{\sin\delta\cos d - \cos\delta\sin d\cos(\alpha-a)\}$$
$$z = r\{\sin\delta\sin d + \cos\delta\cos d\cos(\alpha-a)\}$$

Sun
$$x' = r'\cos\delta'\sin(\alpha'-a)$$
$$y' = r'\{\sin\delta'\cos d - \cos\delta'\sin d\cos(\alpha'-a)\}$$
$$z' = r'\{\sin\delta'\sin d + \cos\delta'\cos d\cos(\alpha'-a)\}$$

But since the z-axis is parallel to the line joining the centres of the Sun and the Moon, we must have $x = x'$ and $y = y'$. The quantities a and d may be calculated from this fact. In an eclipse α', δ' are nearly equal to α, δ, and the explicit determination of a, d makes use of this. Write $b = r/r' = \dfrac{\sin\pi'}{\sin\pi}$. The value of b is about 1/400.

Then from the equations $x = x'$ and $y = y'$ we find on ignoring $(\alpha - a')^2$ and $(\delta - \delta')^2$:

$$a = \alpha' - \frac{b}{1-b} \cos\delta \sec\delta'(\alpha - \alpha'),$$

$$d = \delta' - \frac{b}{1-b}(\delta - \delta').$$

The quantity d is the declination of the axis of the shadow cone, and it is tabulated for every ten minutes during the eclipse in the *Nautical Almanac*, but instead of a a derived quantity μ is given, μ being the hour angle at Greenwich of the axis of the shadow cone. If the sidereal time at Greenwich is S, then $\mu = S - a$.

The angles f_1, f_2 of the penumbral and umbral cones may be found from simple geometry. If R, k are the radii of the Sun and Moon, we have

$$\sin f_1 = \frac{R+k}{r'-r} \quad \text{(penumbral cone)},$$

$$\sin f_2 = \frac{R-k}{r'-r} \quad \text{(umbral cone)}.$$

The radii of the shadows on the fundamental plane may also be found by simple geometry. These radii are defined with an algebraic sign which is positive if the vertex of the cone concerned has a positive z coordinate, i.e. lies between the centre of the Earth and the eclipse: we find then

radius of penumbral cone $l_1 = z \tan f_1 + k \sec f_1$,

radius of umbral cone $l_2 = z \tan f_2 - k \sec f_2$.

Notice that l_1 is always positive but l_2 is positive or negative: if l_2 is negative the eclipse is total and if the eclipse is annular l_2 is positive, but that there are small positive values of l_2 for which the eclipse may just be total at some points.

The Besselian Elements of the Eclipse. These are the co-ordinates on the fundamental plane of the axis of the shadow cone, namely (x, y): the Greenwich hour angle and declination of the direction of the axis of the shadow, μ and d; and the angles and radii on the fundamental plane of the penumbral and umbral cones, or f_1, f_2, l_1, and l_2. The *Nautical Almanac* publishes the Besselian elements for every ten minutes of U.T. during the eclipse, the unit of length being the Earth's equatorial radius. The following table is an abstract of the elements of the eclipse of 1936 June 19.

U.T.	x	y	sin d	cos d	μ			l_1	l_2
h.					°	′	″		
3	−1·25594	+0·64098	+0·39755	+0·91758	224	43	56	+0·54071	−0·00518
4	−0·69929	+0·59667	56	58	239	43	53	087	502
5	−0·14263	+0·55195	57	57	254	43	50	100	490
6	+0·41398	+0·50685	59	57	269	43	47	111	479
7	+0·97049	+0·46137	60	56	284	43	44	119	470

$$\tan f_1 = +0\cdot00460, \qquad \tan f_2 = +0\cdot00458.$$

It will be noticed that d changes very slowly, and μ approximately 15° an hour.

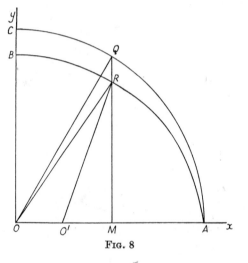

Fɪɢ. 8

The Coordinates on the Fundamental Plane of a Point on the Earth's Surface. Let R be any point on the Earth's surface and ARB a quadrant of the geoid from equator A to pole B passing through R. The geoid is the surface of a tideless ocean and the direction of gravity at R is the normal to the geoid at R.

The geoid is the ellipse

$$\frac{x^2}{1^2} + \frac{y^2}{(1-e^2)} = 1, \text{ where } \sqrt{(1-e^2)} = 0\cdot99664.$$

The gradient of the normal at R is $-\dfrac{dx}{dy} = \dfrac{y}{x(1-e^2)}$.

The geocentric latitude of R is $\angle ROA$ or ϕ', where $\tan\phi' = \dfrac{y}{x}$.

The geographic latitude of R is $\angle RO'A$ or ϕ, where $\tan\phi = \dfrac{y}{x(1-e^2)}$.

The eccentric angle of R is $\angle QOA$ or ϕ_1, where $\tan\phi_1 = \dfrac{y}{x\sqrt{(1-e^2)}}$.

The geographic latitude is obtained from the eccentric angle through $\tan\phi = \tan\phi_1(1-e^2)^{-\frac{1}{2}}$.

The geocentric latitude is obtained from the eccentric angle from

$$\rho\cos\phi' = \cos\phi_1,$$
$$\rho\sin\phi' = \sqrt{(1-e^2)}\sin\phi_1 = 0.99664\sin\phi_1,$$

the unit of distance being the Earth's equatorial radius and ρ the distance of R from the Earth's centre O (Fig. 8).

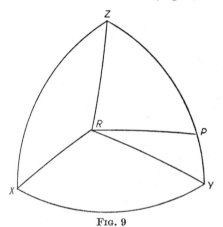

FIG. 9

Now let λ be the longitude of R west of Greenwich. Then the hour angle at R of the axis of the shadow cone is $(\mu-\lambda)$.

Fig. 9 represents the celestial sphere on which Z is parallel to the position of the shadow cone, X and Y the Besselian axes of which X is on the Equator. The Earth's pole P accordingly lies on YZ. The point R represents the longitude west of Greenwich and the geographic latitude of the observer. Then

$$ZPR = \mu-\lambda \quad \text{and} \quad PR = 90°-\phi', \qquad PZ = 90°-d.$$

From this figure one can deduce readily that if ξ, η, ζ are the co-ordinates of the point R on the Earth's surface, we have

$$\xi = \rho\cos RX = \rho\cos\phi'\sin(\mu-\lambda),$$
$$\eta = \rho\cos RY = \rho\sin\phi'\cos d-\rho\cos\phi'\sin d\cos(\mu-\lambda),$$
$$\zeta = \rho\cos RZ = \rho\sin\phi'\sin d+\rho\cos\phi'\cos d\cos(\mu-\lambda).$$

Using the eccentric angle ϕ_1 these become

$$\xi = \cos\phi_1 \sin(\mu-\lambda),$$

$$\eta = 0{\cdot}99664 \cos d \sin\phi_1 - \sin d \cos\phi_1 \cos(\mu-\lambda),$$

$$\zeta = 0{\cdot}99664 \sin d \sin\phi_1 + \cos d \cos\phi_1 \cos(\mu-\lambda).$$

Calculation of the Beginning and End of an Eclipse. In

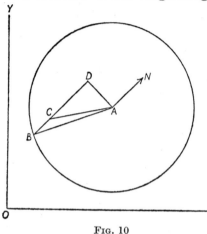

Fig. 10, which represents a plane passing through the observer at C parallel to the fundamental plane at some instant, let A (x,y) be the intersection of the axis of the shadow cone with the plane, and let C (ξ, η) be the position of the observer. The origin is chosen such that the axis OZ passes through the Earth's centre. The umbral and penumbral cones intersect the fundamental plane in circles

centred on A, namely $(X-x)^2+(Y-y)^2 = L^2$, where $L = l_1-\zeta\tan f_1$ or $l_2-\zeta\tan f_2$. The commencement or end of an eclipse is marked by the passage of the appropriate circle through C.

The distance of the observer from the axis of the shadow is the length AC represented by the quantity m, where $m^2 = (\xi-x)^2+(\eta-y)^2$. If the direction $\overrightarrow{CA}$ makes an angle M with the axis OY we have

$$(y-\eta) = m \cos M, \qquad (x-\xi) = m \sin M,$$

(the position angle being reckoned from north through east, or from OY through OX).

Now the magnitude and direction n, N of the vector $\overrightarrow{AN}$ representing the motion of the centre of the shadow relative to the observer are given by

$$(\dot{y}-\dot{\eta}) = n \cos N, \qquad (\dot{x}-\dot{\xi}) = n \sin N.$$

Although the point (ξ, η) is fixed on the Earth's surface, it is not fixed on the fundamental plane which is rotating relatively to the Earth. We have in fact

$$\dot{\xi} = \dot{\mu} \cos\phi_1 \cos(\mu-\lambda),$$

$$\dot{\eta} = \dot{\mu} \cos\phi_1 \sin(\mu-\lambda)\sin d,$$

where $\dot{\mu}$ is the diurnal motion of the quantity μ. Now $\mu = S - a$ and the sidereal time S varies much more rapidly than the quantity a, so that $\dot{\mu}$ is practically the variation in hour angle of an object stationary in right ascension or $15'$ per minute of time. Accordingly we get for the variation of ξ and η per minute of time:

$$\dot{\xi} = \sin 15' \cos \phi_1 \cos(\mu - \lambda) = 0 \cdot 004363 \cos \phi_1 \cos(\mu - \lambda),$$

$$\dot{\eta} = \sin 15' \cos \phi_1 \sin(\mu - \lambda) \sin d = 0 \cdot 004363 \, \xi \sin d.$$

The quantities $\dot{x}$ and $\dot{y}$ are found in practice by taking differences from the tabular values of x and y in the *Nautical Almanac*.

Now suppose that the point B on the edge of the shadow passes through C at a time t minutes after the state of affairs depicted in Fig. 10. Then the vector $\overrightarrow{BC}$ is nt. Let $\angle NAB = \psi$. Projecting AC, AB on to AD ($\perp BC$) we get $m \sin(M - N) = L \sin \psi$, this equation determining the angle ψ. Projecting AC, AB on to CD we get

$$nt = L \cos \psi - m \cos(M - N).$$

Numerical Example. From the map shown in the 1936 *Nautical Almanac* (p. 22) it appears that the eclipse of 1936 June 19 ends at 5^h in the Crimea. We shall here compute the time of end of the eclipse at Simeis Observatory, for which

$$\lambda = -2^h \, 15^m \, 59 \cdot 38^s, \qquad \phi = 44° \, 24' \, 11 \cdot 6'',$$

$$\log \rho \sin \phi' = 9 \cdot 84272, \qquad \log \rho \cos \phi' = 9 \cdot 85470.$$

The Besselian elements of this eclipse have been reproduced on p. 16. From the values of μ and d given there we proceed to compute ξ, η, ζ for the Simeis Observatory at 5^h U.T.

We find

$$\xi = -0 \cdot 67775 \quad | \quad \xi - x = -0 \cdot 53512$$
$$\eta = +0 \cdot 54744 \quad | \quad \eta - y = -0 \cdot 00451$$
$$\zeta = +0 \cdot 48759$$
$$\dot{\xi} = +0 \cdot 001003 \quad | \quad \dot{\xi} - \dot{x} = -0 \cdot 008274$$
$$\dot{\eta} = -0 \cdot 001175 \quad | \quad \dot{\eta} - \dot{y} = -0 \cdot 000427$$

Next, the quantities m, M; n, N must be computed. We get

$$m = 0 \cdot 53514$$
$$M = 89° \, 31'$$
$$n = 0 \cdot 00829$$
$$N = 87° \, 03',$$

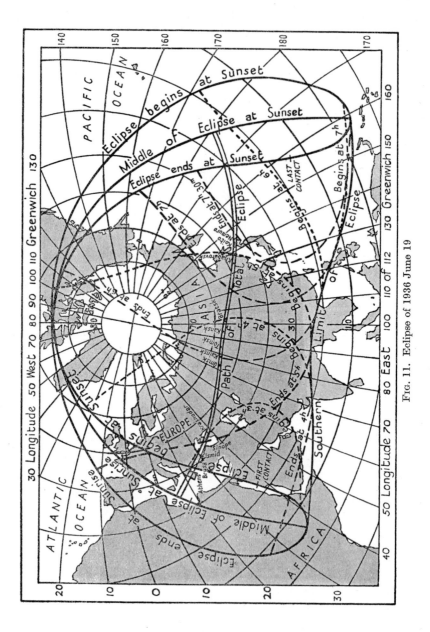

FIG. 11. Eclipse of 1936 June 19

Finally $L = +0.53876$ giving $\psi = 2° \, 27'$.

We get $nt = 0.00363$ so that $t = +0.438^{\mathrm{m}}$. The eclipse ends at Simeis at U.T. $5^{\mathrm{h}} \, 0^{\mathrm{m}} \, 26^{\mathrm{s}}$.

Centre of Track of Total Eclipse. The centre of the eclipse at any instant occurs at the point where $\xi = x$ and $\eta = y$; given the Besselian elements x, y, μ, and d, we can calculate the latitude and longitude of the centre of the eclipse by expressing ξ and η in terms of the latitude and longitude and equating them to x and y, thus:

$$x = \cos\phi_1 \sin(\mu - \lambda),$$

$$y = 0.99664 \cos d \sin\phi_1 - \sin d \cos\phi_1 \cos(\mu - \lambda).$$

The explicit solution for ϕ_1 and λ is

$$\sin\phi_1(1 - e^2\cos^2 d) = y\cos d\sqrt{(1-e^2)} + \sin d\sqrt{\{(1-e^2\cos^2 d)(1-x^2) - y^2\}},$$

from which ϕ_1 can be calculated, and

$$\sin(\mu - \lambda) = x\sec\phi_1,$$

from which we can calculate λ. The geographical latitude ϕ can be computed from the eccentric angle ϕ_1 from the equation

$$\tan\phi = \tan\phi_1\sqrt{(1-e^2)}.$$

The value of $\sqrt{(1-e^2)}$ is 0.99664, so that $e^2 = 0.00671$.

For example, we may calculate the position of the centre of the shadow at 5^{h} U.T. on 1936 June 19.

Here

$$x = -0.14263, \qquad y = +0.55195, \qquad \sin d = 0.39757,$$

$$\cos d = 0.91757, \qquad \mu = 254° \, 43' \, 50''.$$

We find $\phi_1 = 56° \, 36'$, whence $\phi = 56° \, 41'$. Using this value of ϕ_1, $(\mu - \lambda) = -15° \, 1'$, giving $\lambda = -90° \, 15'$.

Duration of Eclipse at Centre and Size of Shadow. The position of the centre of the shadow for every ten minutes of U.T. is tabulated in the *Nautical Almanac*. The duration of the total phase in minutes is given by

$$-2(l_2 - \zeta\tan f_2)/n$$

for all points on the central line. This duration is also given in the *Nautical Almanac*. In the example given above, 1936 June 19 at 5^{h}, we have for $\phi_1 = 56° \, 36'$ and $(\mu - \lambda) = -15° \, 1'$, $\zeta = 0.81868$. This gives $-2(l_2 - \zeta\tan f_2) = +0.01730$ (with the values of l_2 and

$\tan f_2$ given in the $N.A.$). In calculating n from $n^2 = (\dot{\xi}-\dot{x})^2+(\dot{\eta}-\dot{y})^2$ note that

$$\dot{\xi} = 0{\cdot}004363 \cos\phi_1 \cos(\mu-\lambda),$$

and

$$\dot{\eta} = 0{\cdot}004363\xi \sin d$$

for the centre. Then $n = 0{\cdot}006976$, giving a duration of $2{\cdot}48$ minutes or $2^m 29^s$.

The shadow of the Moon on the Earth has a breadth $2(l_2-\zeta\tan f_2)$ in a direction perpendicular to the Sun's azimuth. In the direction of the Sun's azimuth it is lengthened by projection by a factor equal to the cosecant of the Sun's altitude, or, treating the Earth as spherical, the major axis of the elliptic shadow is $2(l_2-\zeta\tan f_2)/\zeta$.

Using Hayford's value of 3,963 miles for the Earth's equatorial radius, we find $83{\cdot}9$ miles and $68{\cdot}6$ miles for the major and minor axes of the ellipse at 5^h on 1936 June 19.

The boundaries of the band over which the eclipse is total may be found approximately as follows:

At Greenwich time t a point ξ, η, ζ on the edge of the shadow is given by

$$(\xi-x)^2+(\eta-y)^2 = (l_2-\zeta\tan f_2)^2.$$

The envelope of these circles is found by combining this equation with

$$(\dot{\xi}-\dot{x})(\xi-x)+(\dot{\eta}-\dot{y})(\eta-y) = 0,$$

for the variation of l_2 is negligible, as is that of $\zeta\tan f_2$, $\dot{\xi}$, and $\dot{\eta}$ may be assumed to be the same as at the point x, y on the central line.

Thus

$$\xi-x = \pm(l_2-\zeta\tan f_2)\cos N,$$
$$\eta-y = \mp(l_2-\zeta\tan f_2)\sin N,$$

where

$$\tan N = +\frac{\dot{x}-\dot{\xi}}{\dot{y}-\dot{\eta}},$$

and ζ may be taken to have the value which it has at the point x, y on the central line.

The points when the eclipse begins or ends at sunrise or sunset are obtained with sufficient accuracy by a graphical solution. The direction of Z is on the horizon. The coordinate ζ is zero and, assuming a spherical earth, $\xi^2+\eta^2 = 1$. The points of intersection of this circle with the shadow $(\xi-x)^2+(\eta-y)^2 = L^2$ gives the position of ξ and η for all the times for which x and y have been calculated. Then ϕ and $\mu-\lambda$ are given by

$$\sin\phi = \eta\cos d$$

and

$$\sin(\mu-\lambda) = \xi\sec\phi.$$

Exact solutions for the various circumstances of eclipses are given in Chauvenet's *Astronomy*. Simplifications of the formulae are given by Comrie,† but a number of subsidiary quantities are still required which to a certain extent make the problem seem rather complicated. The formula on p. 21 offers a convenient mode of calculation for all points on the central line, as the factor $1 - e^2 \cos^2 d$ may be taken as constant throughout the eclipse. The diagram taken from the *Nautical Almanac* of 1936 shows the general features of a solar eclipse.

† *M.N.R.A.S.* **93,** 175 (1933).

IV

THE SAROS

CHALDEAN astronomers discovered that eclipses, both solar and lunar, recur after 223 months or 18 years 10 or 11 days, depending on the number of leap years in the interval. This discovery was probably facilitated by the use of a lunar calendar. From the accession of Nabonassar, king of Babylon, in 747 B.C. a record was kept of astronomical phenomena occurring each month. The recurrence of eclipses was known in the sixth century B.C.† According to Herodotus, Thales predicted an eclipse which has been dated by modern astronomers as occurring in 585 B.C. on May 28. If this is correct, Thales used the Saros for his prediction.

This remarkable cycle arises from a relationship between the length of the month—i.e. the interval from new Moon to new Moon or full Moon to full Moon—and the period of revolution of the Moon's nodes. As seen in Chapter II, eclipses only occur when the Moon is new or full near one of the nodes of its path.

The mean length of the month from full Moon to full Moon is 29·53059 days. If the Moon's orbit were stationary, the Sun would pass through corresponding nodes of the Moon's orbit at intervals of one year, but owing to the regression of the nodes of the Moon's orbit round the ecliptic, the Sun passes in fact through corresponding nodes in a period shorter than one year, namely, 346·62 days.

Now $223 \times 29 \cdot 53059$ days $= 6585 \cdot 32$ days

and $19 \times 346 \cdot 62$ days $= 6585 \cdot 78$ days,

so that after an interval of 6585·32 days, new and full Moons will recur. If the new Moon were actually in the node at the beginning of one Saros, it will precede the node by 0·46 day at the beginning of the next. In this time the Sun moves through 0·46/346·62 of 360° or 29′, and will thus be only 29′ from the node at the time of new Moon. Thus eclipses will recur in a very long sequence—viz. until the Sun has had time to move so far away from the node that it is outside the ecliptic limit.

There is an additional relationship which makes the Saros still more remarkable. An eclipse of long duration follows an eclipse of long duration, the change from one to a second eclipse of the sequence

† 'The Calendar', an article in the *Nautical Almanac* for 1931, by Dr. Fotheringham.

being very small. This arises from the fact that the Moon's distance
and consequently its apparent diameter has changed but a small
amount in the interval of a Saros. The orbit of the Moon has a
large eccentricity, but the ellipse revolves so that its apse or nearest
point to the Earth makes a complete revolution in 8·85 years. Owing
to this forward movement the Moon is nearest to the Earth at intervals of 27·55455 days. If this number be multiplied by 239, we
obtain 6585·54 days, differing only 0·22 day from the Saros. In this
time the Moon only moves between 2° and 3°, and its diameter at
the most can only change 3″. The eccentricity of the Sun's orbit is
small, but as the Saros is 11 days later a change of 5″ in the diameter
is possible in April or October, when the distance is changing rapidly.
Generally the changes in apparent diameter are much smaller. Thus
in six eclipses of long duration of the present century we find for
semi-diameters of Moon and Sun calculated by Sadler at the Nautical
Almanac Office:

	Moon	Sun	Duration
	′ ″	′ ″	m.
1901 May 18	16 36·1	15 48·4	6·5
1919 May 29	37·5	46·6	6·8
1937 June 8	38·7	45·2	7·1
1955 June 20	39·5	44·3	7·2
1973 June 30	40·5	43·8	7·2
1991 July 11	41·2	43·9	7·3

The remarkable character of the Saros is best seen by comparing
the dates and durations in successive intervals of 18 years 11 days.
The Saros for 1900–18 is given below in comparison with that for
the following period. In this table the longest duration of the eclipse
is given in minutes of time where the eclipse is total or annular and
for partial eclipses the fraction of the area of the obscured portion
of the Sun is given. For lunar eclipses the greatest fraction of the
area of the eclipse is given for partial phases, and the magnitude of
a total eclipse in a corresponding manner.

Examination of this table is instructive, as showing the general
relationship between solar and lunar eclipses. In the years 1904, 1908,
1911, and 1915, and the corresponding years in the next cycle, there
are two total or annular eclipses of the Sun and none of the Moon.
In 1902, 1906, 1913, 1916–17, 1917, 1924, 1928, 1931, and 1935 there
are total eclipses of the Moon between *two* partial eclipses of the Sun.
The close relationship in the duration of the totality in successive

Eclipses in the Saros, 1900 May 28 to 1918 June 8, compared with those in the succeeding Saros.

Solar Eclipses				Lunar Eclipses	
			m. or mag.		mag.
1900 May 28	1918 June 8	T.	2·2; 2·4	June 13; June 24 P. 0·00;	0·14
Nov. 21	Dec. 3	A.	6·5; 7·1		
1901 May 18	1919 May 29	T.	6·5; 6·8		
Nov. 11	Nov. 22	A.	10·5; 11·6	Oct. 27; Nov. 8 P. 0·23;	0·18
1902 Apr. 8⎫	..	P.	0·07; ..	Apr. 22; May 3 T. 1·34;	1·22
May 7⎭	1920 May 18	P.	0·86; 0·97		
Oct. 31	Nov. 10	P.	0·70; 0·74	Oct. 16; Oct. 27 T. 1·46;	1·40
1903 May 29	1921 Apr. 8	A.	1·8; 1·7	Apr. 11; Apr. 22 P. 0·97; T. 1·07
Sept. 21	Oct. 1	T.	2·1; 1·9	Oct. 6; Oct. 16 P. 0·87;	0·94
1904 Mar. 17	1922 Mar. 28	A.	7·9; 7·8		
Sept. 9	Sept. 21	T.	5·5; 6·0		
1905 Mar. 6	1923 Mar. 17	A.	7·7; 7·9	Feb. 19; Mar. 3 P. 0·41;	0·38
Aug. 30	Sept. 10	T.	3·7; 3·6	Aug. 14; Aug. 26 P. 0·29;	0·17
1906 Feb. 22	1924 Mar. 5	P.	0·54; 0·58		
July 21⎫	July 31⎫	P.	0·34; 0·19	Aug. 3; Aug. 14 T. 1·63;	1·61
Aug. 20⎭	Aug. 30⎭	P.	0·32; 0·43		
1907 Jan. 14	1925 Jan. 24	T.	2·3; 2·5	Jan. 28; Feb. 8 P. 0·72;	0·74
July 10	July 20	A.	6·8; 7·2	July 24; Aug. 4 P. 0·62;	0·75
1908 Jan. 3	1926 Jan. 14	T.	4·2; 4·2		
June 28	July 9	A.	3·8; 3·9		
Dec. 23	1927 Jan. 3	A.–T.; A. 0·8			
1909 June 17	June 29	T.	0·8; 0·8	June 3; June 15 T. 1·16;	1·02
Dec. 12	Dec. 24	P.	0·54; 0·55	Nov. 26; Dec. 8 T. 1·37;	1·36
1910 May 9	1928 May 19⎫	T.	very short	May 23; June 3 T. 1·10;	1·25
..	June 17⎭	.. P. 0·04			
Nov. 2	Nov. 12	P.	0·85; 0·81	Nov. 16; Nov. 27 T. 1·13;	1·16
1911 Apr. 28	1929 May 9	T.	5·0; 5·1		
Oct. 22	Nov. 1	A.	3·8; 4·0		
1912 Apr. 17	1930 Apr. 28	A.–T.; A.–T.		Apr. 1; Apr. 13 P. 0·19;	0·11
Oct. 10	Oct. 21	T.	2·3; 1·9	Sept. 25; Oct. 7 P. 0·12;	0·03
1913 Apr. 6	1931 Apr. 18	P.	0·43; 0·51	Mar. 22; Apr. 2 T. 1·58;	1·51
Aug. 31⎫	Sept. 12⎫	P.	0·15; 0·05	Sept. 15; Sept. 26 T. 1·44;	1·43
Sept. 29⎭	Oct. 11⎭	P.	0·83; 0·90		
1914 Feb. 25	1932 Mar. 7	A.short; A.short		Mar. 11; Mar. 22 P. 0·92;	0·97
Aug. 21	Aug. 31	T.	2·2; 1·7	Sept. 4; Sept. 14 P. 0·86;	0·98
1915 Feb. 14	1933 Feb. 24	A.	2·1; 1·5		
Aug. 10	Aug. 21	A.	1·4; 2·1		
1916 Feb. 3	1934 Feb. 14	T.	2·6; 2·9	Jan. 19; Jan. 30 P. 0·14;	0·12
July 30	Aug. 10	A.	6·4; 6·6	July 15; July 26 P. 0·80;	0·67
Dec. 24⎫	1935 Jan. 5⎫	P.	0·01; 0·00		
1917 Jan. 23⎭	Feb. 3⎭	P.	0·72; 0·74	Jan. 8; Jan. 19 T. 1·37;	1·36
June 19⎫	June 30⎫	P.	0·47; 0·34	July 4; July 16 T. 1·62;	1·76
July 19⎭	July 30⎭	P.	0·09; 0·23		
Dec. 14	Dec. 25	A.short; A.short		Dec. 28; Jan. 8 T. 1·01;	1·02

cycles is especially well brought out. A nearly total eclipse of the Moon in 1903 April 11 is succeeded by one just total in 1921 April 22. The last eclipse of a cycle occurred on 1902 April 8, and the first of a new cycle began on 1928 June 17. In all other cases an eclipse occurred in both cycles 1900–18 and 1918–36.

The eclipse of 1902 April 8 was the last of a cycle of 76 eclipses, beginning A.D. 550 January 3, when a small partial eclipse occurred near the South Pole. This was followed by 12 partial eclipses gradually increasing in size and travelling northward from A.D. 568 to

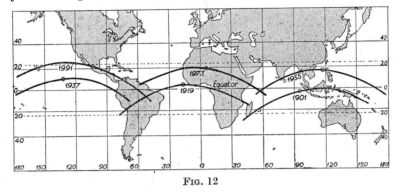

FIG. 12

A.D. 766. These were followed by 19 annular eclipses from A.D. 784 to A.D. 1096; then by 5 eclipses from 1108 to 1181 which were annular or total, then by 19 total eclipses from A.D. 1199 to A.D. 1523, and finally by 21 partial eclipses from A.D. 1541 to A.D. 1902, which became less and less, till the shadow in 1920 just missed the North Pole.

In a similar manner if we follow the lunar eclipse of magnitude 0·23 on 1901 October 27 and 0·18 on 1919 November 8, we find that it began as a partial eclipse near the South Pole on 1126 July 6, and was followed by 8 partial eclipses; it was then followed by 26 total eclipses from 1288 to 1739 attaining greatest magnitude in 1631, and followed by 19 partial eclipses, the last being a very small one which will occur near the North Pole on 2082 February 13.

The number of repetitions of solar eclipses is more than 70 and of lunar eclipses more than 50 over a range of 1,300 or 900 years approximately in the two cases.

Another feature in the Saros to which attention may be drawn is the regular change in longitude at successive eclipses. In the interval of 0·32 day the Earth turns nearly through 120°, and the eclipse tracks are displaced westward by approximately this amount. Fig. 12 shows the effect in the six long eclipses of the twentieth century.†

† Reference may be made to an article in *Nature*, June 18, 1928, by Jackson. The same number contains a series of interesting articles by astronomers and physicists.

Metonic Cycle. The synodic month, i.e. the mean interval from new Moon to new Moon, is 29·53059 days, and the tropical year is 365·2422 days. Thus 235 synodic months contain 6939·69 days and 19 tropical years contain 6939·60 days. The Sun and Moon therefore both return to the same longitude after 19 years. But 20 revolutions of the Moon's node take 6932·40 days. If the Moon was at its node at a given date, it will be 7·20 days or 7·5° from the node after 19 years have elapsed. Thus a short cycle of 4 or 5 eclipses may occur at intervals of 19 years. This cycle is of interest because the eclipse occurs in the same part of the sky. Thus the favourable field in the Hyades for the deflexion of light in 1919 May belonged to a cycle which started in 1881, and will continue till 1938. Reference to the table on p. 26 shows frequent recurrence of eclipses in 19 years at the same time of year.

ECLIPSES OF THE MOON

Lunar Eclipses in Antiquity; the Shape of the Earth. Eclipses of the Moon were of great importance in ancient times as they revealed the spherical form of the Earth and later permitted an estimate of the distance of the Moon from the Earth.

Parmenides, a philosopher of the Pythagorean school who flourished about 500 B.C., taught that the Earth was of spherical form. He probably made this great discovery from the reports of travellers that more stars became circumpolar as they went North and new stars became visible as they went South. Towards the end of the fifth century eclipses of the Moon were attributed by Pythagorean philosophers to the Moon's passage through the shadow of the Earth. This explanation was somewhat weakened by their hypothesis of another body, the 'antichthon', which was assumed to cast a shadow in certain cases and thus explain why lunar eclipses were more frequent than solar eclipses. Aristotle, whose astronomical knowledge was based on Eudoxus and Kalippus, definitely states that as the edge of the shadow of the Earth on the Moon is always circular, the Earth must be a sphere. It seems certain that this doctrine was accepted by Greek astronomers at least as early as 350 B.C.†

Aristarchus of Samos, who lived about 250 B.C., made an attempt to determine the distance of the Moon from the Earth by comparing the apparent radius of the shadow with that of the Moon, but obtained a wrong result from an over-estimate of the Moon's diameter.

Hipparchus (150 B.C.), with a more correct value of the Moon's diameter, obtained a very good value of the Moon's distance in terms of the Earth's radius. It is easily seen by drawing the circumscribing cone of the Sun and Earth that the sum of the parallaxes of the Moon and Sun equals the sum of the angular semi-diameter of the shadow and of the Sun.

Assuming the distance of the Sun to be many times that of the Moon, its parallax is at once found from the apparent radii of the shadow and the Sun.

† Dreyer, *Planetary Systems*.

In the *De Revolutionibus* of Copernicus the mode of proof used by Hipparchus is perhaps reproduced. The diagram is copied from that work.[†] The centre of the Sun is at D, that of the Earth at K, the vertex of the shadow cone at S. ADC is the diameter of the Sun, GKE of the Earth, and QMR of the shadow cone at the distance of the Moon.

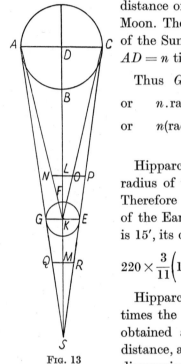

Then $GK-QM : AD-GK = MK : KD$. Let us suppose that the distance of the Sun is n times the distance of the Moon. Then $KD=nMK$. Also the apparent radii of the Sun and Moon are nearly the same. Thus $AD = n$ times the radius of the Moon.

Thus $GK-QM : n.\text{radius of Moon}-GK = 1 : n$

or $n.\text{radius of Moon}-GK = n.GK-n.QM$

or $n(\text{radius of Moon}+\text{radius of shadow})$
$$= (n+1).\text{radius of Earth.}$$

Hipparchus found from observation that the radius of the shadow was $\frac{8}{3}$ radius of the Moon. Therefore radius of the Moon $= \frac{3}{11}(1+1/n)$ radius of the Earth. As the angular radius of the Moon is $15'$, its distance is 220 times its radius and is

$$220 \times \frac{3}{11}\left(1+\frac{1}{n}\right) \quad \text{or} \quad 60\left(1+\frac{1}{n}\right) \text{ radius of the Earth.}$$

Hipparchus assumed that the Sun was 20 or 30 times the distance of the Moon, and in this way obtained an approximate value of the Moon's distance, and definitely a minimum distance. The

Fig. 13

discoveries of the spherical form of the Earth and the distance of the Moon are by far the most important results obtained from the study of lunar eclipses.

Colour of the Moon during an Eclipse. The time from the entrance of the Moon into the shadow of the Earth to its emergence is seldom more than three hours. It is totally eclipsed for not more than half this time. At such a time it is seldom, if ever, invisible to the naked eye. Generally it is of a copper colour.

As seen from the Moon, the Earth will be enclosed by a narrow reddish ring, unless the section of the Earth at right angles to the

[†] This reference was obtained from Berry's *Short History of Astronomy*, p. 50.

direction of the Moon is covered with dense clouds. The radius of
the geometrical shadow of the Earth at the Moon's mean distance
is 41' and at most 46'. A ray of light tangential at the Earth's surface
is refracted by about 40', and remembering that the Sun's diameter
is 16', the centre of the shadow will always receive some light.
Fesenkov,† using such data as are available for temperature in the
Earth's atmosphere, gives the following table for refraction and
absorption for 5,500 A.

Height	Refr.	Abs.	Height	Refr.	Abs.
km.	'	m.	km.	'	m.
0	39·9	6·99	7	17·0	2·82
1	34·2	6·09	10	12·4	1·86
2	29·0	5·40	14	7·3	0·97
3	25·4	4·66	21	1·9	0·26
4	23·0	4·12	31	0·4	0·05
5	20·9	3·65	41	0·1	0·01

He next notes that in addition to the atmospheric dispersion for
different wave-lengths there is also a dispersion dR/dh, depending
on the fact that owing to the sensible diameter of the Sun, light passes
through the atmosphere at heights where refraction and absorption
differ.

   Taking this into account he finds a somewhat complicated expression for the illumination at any point in the shadow. From this he
deduces that the diminution of the intensity for 5,500 A., expressed
in stellar magnitudes, is:

Distance from centre of shadow	0'	5'	10'	15'	25'	41'
	m.	m.	m.	m.	m.	m.
Magnitude	14·58	14·35	13·45	12·26	10·19	6·00

   This theoretical result may be compared with observations made
at the eclipses of 1921, 1924, 1928, and 1931.

   Danjon‡ made visual observations through yellow and green filters
of the eclipse of 1921 October 16–17. He used a Wollaston doubly
refracting prism and placed the two images of the Moon side by side.
By use of a nicol he compared the intensity of the light near the
Moon's edge in the umbra with that of the uneclipsed edge of the
Moon, or with the edge in the penumbra. Then, by additional
observations, compared the penumbra with the uneclipsed edge of

† *Bulletin of the Academy of Sciences, U.S.S.R.*, No. 1, 1932.
‡ *C.R.* **173**, 706 (1921).

the Moon. He gives the following results, converted into stellar magnitudes:

Umbra			Penumbra		
Distance (from centre of shadow)	6,100 A.	5,400 A.	Distance (from centre of shadow)	Obs.	Calc.
	m.	m.		m.	m.
12′	9·8	11·5	40·7′	6·2	..
20	9·5	10·4	42·5	4·2	..
30	9·2	9·8	45	2·8	2·6
35	8·9	9·4	50	1·5	1·7
40	7·2	7·3	60	0·5	0·5
40·7	6·2	6·2	70	0·1	0·1
..	..	..	73·4	0·0	0·0

Extrapolating to the centre of the shadow he finds for yellow light $10 \cdot 2^m$ and for green light $13 \cdot 0^m$. If the eclipse had been central, the total light of the Moon would have been equivalent to a star of $-2 \cdot 6^m$.

Dufay and Conder,[†] observing the eclipse of 1924 August 14 at an altitude of 1,070 metres, found the eclipsed part of the Moon visible during the partial phase. They describe the colour of the umbra as grey-green at the edge, increasing through orange-red to brown-red. Using a photometer, with which they were able to compare the total light with starlight, they find for different distances of its centre from the centre of the shadow:

	10′	12′	14′	16′	18′	20′	22′	24′
	m.	m.	m.	m.	m.	m.	m.	m.
Visual light . .	−0·9	−1·0	−1·1	−1·2	−1·4	−1·6	−2·1	−2·7
Photographic light .	..	+3·2	+2·3	+1·4	+0·7	0·0	−0·7	..

taking the visual magnitude of the full Moon as $-12 \cdot 55^m$.

Keenan,[‡] at the eclipse of 1928 November 27, used four filters transmitting light from 3,800 A. to 4,200 A. and 4,600 A. to 5,000 A., 4,000 A. to 4,900 A., 5,000 A. to 5,900 A., and a Kryptocyanine plate transmitting light round 7,600 A. The shadow had a radius of 45·0′, and the centre of the Moon at mid-eclipse was 24′ from the centre. The differences of intensity from the uneclipsed Moon in stellar magnitudes are shown on p. 33.

The very striking difference between the extreme red and the other filters is apparent.

† *C.R.* **180**, 194 (1925).   ‡ *P.A.S.P.* **41**, 297 (1929).

3,800 A.–4,200 A. and 4,600 A.–5,000 A.		4,000 A.–4,900 A.		5,000 A.–5,900 A.		Round 7,600 A.	
Dist.[1]	Mag.[2]	Dist.	Mag.	Dist.	Mag.	Dist.	Mag.
	m.		m.		m.		m.
40·7′	8·23	39·3′	8·12	39·3′	8·17	38·6′	6·48
36·0	8·62	34·2	8·96	33·8	9·25	37·1	6·82
30·9	9·31	29·1	9·71	28·8	9·72	32·4	7·41
25·4	10·10	23·6	10·39	23·3	10·34	27·3	7·72
20·4	10·48	17·8	11·46	..	..	22·6	7·81

[1] From centre of shadow.   [2] Difference from uneclipsed moon.

Barabascheff and Semegken[†] at the eclipse of 1931 April 2, when the radius of the shadow was 45·2′, by use of red and blue filters obtained the following values for the decrease of intensity at different distances from the centre of the shadow, reckoned in stellar magnitudes.

Distance	4,630 A.	6,340 A.
	m.	m.
33·9′	..	9·06
32·5	..	9·25
31·2	11·20	9·44
29·8	11·46	9·70
28·5	11·69	9·88
27·1	11·92	10·16
25·8	12·13	10·34
24·4	12·39	10·52
23·1	12·74	10·80
21·7	13·05	..
20·4	13·81	..

Other observations of the difference between the total visual light of the eclipsed and full Moon, expressed in stellar magnitudes, at several recent eclipses are:

	Magnitude of Eclipse	Difference	
		m.	
1921 Oct. 16	0·938	8·76	Hopman[‡]
1924 Aug. 14	1·659	10·18	Barabascheff[‖]
1927 Dec. 8	1·358	9·48	..
1926 June 25	..	0·92 (penumbral)	..

With Russell's value of $-12\cdot3^m$ for the stellar magnitude of the full Moon, the eclipsed Moon has a total visual brightness varying from Venus to Sirius.

[†] Zs. f. Astrophys. **6**, 114 (1932).   [‡] A.N. **215**, 269 (1922).
[‖] A.N. **233**, 213 (1934).

Willard Fisher† has collected observations of the brightness of lunar eclipses from 1860 to 1922, for the purpose of finding data on the transmission of light through different layers of the Earth's atmosphere. He grades the observations into three classes, according to whether details on the Moon can be seen with the naked eye, a 2-inch telescope, or a 6-inch telescope. The argument for this procedure is that although the illumination is unaltered, the difference of scale has a considerable effect on the visibility of small objects. He then groups the observations in various ways and concludes that the eclipsed Moon is generally brighter when it is south of the centre of the shadow, and that volcanic dust has had an effect in diminishing the visibility. No effect of the size of the shadow is found.

Spectrum of Eclipsed Moon. The spectrum of the eclipsed Moon was observed at the Lick Observatory by Moore and Brigham.‡ They gave an exposure of 20 minutes from a point on the edge of the shadow to 1·5′ within it, and compared this with an exposure of 1 second on the uneclipsed Moon. They find a very marked difference in the intensities at the violet and red end of the spectrum which extended from 3,800 A. to 6,900 A., and that water vapour and oxygen lines are strongly accentuated. These, as the observers remark, agree with anticipation.

Occultations. Total eclipses of the Moon are of service in the observation of occultations. Not only are fainter stars observable, but disappearance and reappearance of the same star at the dark limbs of the Moon are obtained. In this way the diameter of the Moon may be found. When the diameter is determined at full Moon with a meridian instrument, a slightly larger value, owing to irradiation at the limbs, is usually found. At eclipses of the Sun, on the contrary, a smaller value is found, as the eclipse is not total till the light coming through valleys on the Moon's limb, known as Baily's beads, has ceased. Occultations give a mean value, allowing for irregularities in the Moon's surface. This value is used for all observations of occultations in finding the position of the centre of the Moon. As these occultations are usually taken at the dark limb in the first half of the lunation, it is important to have a correct value of the Moon's diameter.

Observations of Temperature. The most valuable observations taken in a lunar eclipse are concerned with the fall of temperature

† Harvard Reprint No. 7.　　　　　　‡ *P.A.S.P.* **39**, 223 (1927).

on the Moon as it passes into the shadows. In the eclipse of 1927 June 14 Pettit and Nicholson† made a continuous series of measurements of the radiation of a point which passed near the centre of the shadow, using a vacuum thermocouple on the 100-inch mirror at Mount Wilson. They concluded that the temperature (absolute) fell from 342° to 175° K. during the partial phase, continued to drop to 156° K. during totality, and rose abruptly to nearly the original temperature during the last partial phase. From the rapidity of these changes, they concluded that only a very small amount of radiant energy is conducted into the Moon from its surface.

H. N. Russell‡ makes the following comments: 'Those rapid changes [of temperature] show that the cooling was only skin-deep, and that the superficial material of the Moon must be a very poor conductor of heat—much worse than any sort of solid rock, and comparable to pumice, or volcanic ashes. While the surface is hotter than boiling water, or almost as cold as liquid air, the temperature a foot below probably varies but a few degrees from an average near the freezing-point.'

† *Ap. J.* **71**, 102 (1930).
‡ *The Solar System and its Origin* (New York, 1935), p. 49.

VI

THE SECULAR ACCELERATION

Discovery by Halley. Dunthorne's Determination of Amount.
In 1693 Halley,[†] by comparing ancient eclipses of the Moon given
in the *Almagest* and eclipses observed by Arabian astronomers in
the ninth century with those in his own time, made the suggestion
that the Moon's mean motion appeared to have a secular acceleration. He did not, however, fix the amount. It was not till 1749 that
the matter was reopened by Dunthorne,[‡] who investigated two solar
eclipses and a lunar eclipse observed at Cairo in the tenth century,
an eclipse observed by Theon in A.D. 364, an eclipse of the Moon
observed in Alexandria in 201 B.C., and one observed at Babylon in
721 B.C. His conclusion was that if the acceleration be taken as
uniform, and the observations were not sufficient to prove the
contrary, the secular acceleration of the Moon's mean longitude was
$+10'' T^2$, where T is measured in centuries. Mayer and Lalande
obtained similar results shortly afterwards.

Laplace's Explanation. The Academy of Sciences offered prizes
for the discovery of the physical cause of this phenomenon. Euler,
Lagrange, and Laplace received prizes for their memoirs but failed
to find the true explanation. Suggestions were made that the cause
was a resisting medium, or possibly a retardation in the Earth's
rotation. Laplace dismissed the former, as such resistance would
be shown by the planets, and avoided the latter till he was satisfied
that all gravitational consequences had been sufficiently explored.
Laplace's explanation may be briefly stated as follows. The mean
central disturbing force of the Sun, by which the Moon's gravity
towards the Earth is diminished, depends not only on the Sun's
mean distance but on the eccentricity of the Earth's orbit. Now this
eccentricity is at present diminishing and has been doing so for many
ages, while the mean distance remains unaltered. In consequence of
this, the mean disturbing force is also diminishing and therefore the
Moon's gravity towards the Earth is, on the whole, increasing. Also,
the area described in a given time by the Moon about the Earth is
not affected by this alteration of the central force. Hence it follows
that the Moon's mean distance from the Earth will be diminished in

[†] *Phil. Trans.* **17**, 913 (1693).   [‡] Ibid. **46**, [162] (1749).

the same ratio as the force at a given distance is increased, and the mean angular motion will be increased in double the same ratio.

Laplace found the change in the eccentricity of the Earth's orbit given by
$$e' = e_0' - \alpha t,$$

where t is reckoned in Julian years from 1850·0 and $\alpha = 4\cdot245 \times 10^{-7}$. In this way Laplace found for the secular acceleration
$$\sigma = \tfrac{3}{2}m^2 e_0' \cdot n_0 \alpha,$$

where m is the ratio of the mean motions of the Earth and the Moon, e_0' the eccentricity of the Earth's orbit, n_0 the Moon's mean motion.

Correction by Adams. The result was a secular acceleration of $+11\cdot1'' T^2$, in substantial agreement with Dunthorne's determination from ancient eclipses. Plana[†] and Damoiseau confirmed Laplace's result by carrying it to a further approximation, but in 1853[‡] Adams found that they had committed an error by integrating the differential equations as though e' were constant. He found $\tfrac{3}{2}m^2 - \tfrac{3771}{64}m^4$ as a further approximation to $\tfrac{3}{2}m^2$ given by Laplace, giving $8\cdot3'' T^2$ for the secular acceleration, while Plana had given $\tfrac{3}{2}m^2 - \tfrac{2187}{128}m^4$, or a secular variation of $10\cdot0''$. Adams's value was confirmed by Delaunay. Adams and Delaunay carried the approximation farther, and as all the terms were negative the secular acceleration was still further reduced. The present value given by Brown[||] is $+7\cdot14'' T^2$.

The study of ancient eclipses was pursued by Baily[††] in 1811, who pointed out their use for chronology. Provided that the movements of Sun and Moon are given perfectly by theory, the position of the narrow track where a solar eclipse is total can be calculated. It would generally be a rare occurrence for an eclipse to be total at the same place twice in fifty years. Now a total eclipse is far more striking than a partial eclipse or even an annular eclipse and may well be referred to in ancient records, which sometimes state that stars were visible in which case there can be no doubt of the totality of the eclipse. Baily attempted to determine the date of a famous eclipse mentioned by Herodotus as occurring during a battle between the Medes and Lydians. The place where the battle occurred was not given, but using the best evidence he had for the locality and

[†] Tisserand, *Méc. Celeste*, t. iii, p. 246.   [‡] *Phil. Trans.* **143**, 397 (1853).
[||] *Tables of Motion of Moon*, p. 28.   [††] *Phil. Trans.* **101**, 220 (1811).

taking $+10'' T^2$ as the secular variation the date was identified as
-609 September 30. Unfortunately it was impossible to make the
same secular acceleration fit the eclipse of Agathocles. This eclipse was
seen by the Athenian fleet the day after it left Syracuse, but it is
uncertain whether the fleet sailed north or south of Sicily. Stars were
seen, so that the eclipse was undoubtedly total. There is no doubt
about the identification of the date as -309 August 15.

Airy† determined the secular acceleration from consideration of
early eclipses in 1853 and again in 1857 when the new tables of
the Moon by Hansen were available. He regarded the eclipse of
-309 August 15 as a definite starting-point, and concluded that the
date of the eclipse of Thales was -584 May 28. Airy identified a
passage of Xenophon as indicating a total eclipse which occurred at
Larissa during the war between the Medes and Persians. This he
dates as the eclipse of -546 May 14. His conclusion is that the
secular acceleration is between $+12'' T^2$ and $+13'' T^2$. Hansen was
in close agreement with Airy.

In 1878 Newcomb, in his *Researches on the Motion of the Moon*,‡
made a careful study of supposed total eclipses of the Sun described
by ancient authors with a view to determining slow changes in the
lunar elements. He came to a strongly negative conclusion. Not
only did there appear to be no ancient eclipse of which it could be
concluded that it really was total at a given place, but the accounts
were generally so vague that they were only useful for chronological
or for historical purposes. Rejecting all other records of eclipses
Newcomb based his determination of the secular acceleration on
19 lunar eclipses given in the *Almagest* occurring between -720 and
$+136$, a series of 28 eclipses observed by Arabian astronomers in
Baghdad or Cairo from 829 to 1004, observations of occultations
at Paris from 1621 to 1652, and modern meridian observations. He
finds for the secular acceleration a value $+8 \cdot 8'' T^2$.

Ginzel‖ in 1883 collected materials relating to 45 total eclipses
of the Sun from the records of monasteries and other sources from
346 to 1415. In many cases it is stated that stars were seen. There
is no ambiguity about the totality or the place. He concluded with
a value $+11 \cdot 47'' T^2$ for the secular acceleration.

---

† *Memoirs R.A.S.* **26**, 31 (1857).
‡ Washington, U.S. Naval Observatory, *Observations*, 1875, App. II.
‖ *Vienna Acad. of Sciences, Sitz.* **88**, 629 (1883).

Secular Variation of the Sun's Longitude. Cowell[†] in 1905 gave a new value to the ancient eclipses by deriving not only the secular acceleration of the Moon but also a further element which he at first assumed to be a secular acceleration of the Moon's node, but altered shortly afterwards to a secular acceleration of the Sun, which has the same effect on the positions of the line of totality. He used 5 eclipses, the first being an inscription on a tablet found in Babylon translated by King of the British Museum. 'On the 26th day of the month Sivar in the 7th year, the day was turned into night, and fire in the midst of heaven.' This he identifies as −1062 July 31. He adds the eclipse of −762 June 15, referred to by a tablet at Nineveh; the eclipse of −647 April 6, observed by Archilochus in the island of Thasos; an eclipse of −430 August 3 referred to by Thucydides and supposed total at Athens; and one in Utica on +197 June 3 referred to by Tertullian.

From these eclipses Cowell found a secular acceleration of $+11'' T^2$ in the longitude of the Moon and one of $+4'' T^2$ in that of the Sun.

Newcomb regarded the acceleration of the Sun as contrary to theory, and considered that the eclipses were accounted for as an accidental coincidence, in view of the uncertainties attaching to the evidence.

Fotheringham's Investigation. Fotheringham[‡] gave in 1920 a very complete discussion of ancient eclipses as far as they are available for the determination of secular accelerations. This valuable memoir deals with the following eclipses:

Babylon	−1062 July 31.	Agathocles	−309 August 15.
Nineveh	−762 June 15.	Hipparchus	−128 November 20.
Archilochus	−647 April 6.	Phlegon	+29 November 24.
Thales	−584 May 28.	Plutarch	+71 March 20.
Pindar	−462 April 30.	Theon	+364 June 16.
Thucydides	−430 August 3.		

He rejects the Larissa eclipse of −546 May 14 as a darkening due to some other cause, and the eclipse at Utica (+197 June 3) as being a partial phase of an annular eclipse. Fotheringham gives the name of the author of the first identification of the original record with the supposed eclipse, and enters fully into all the historical circumstances as to where the eclipse was or might have been observed. A diagram

† *M.N.R.A.S.* **45**, 861 (1905).   ‡ *M.N.R.A.S.* **81**, 104 (1920).

in his paper shows that the secular acceleration of the Moon must lie between $+9'' T^2$ and $12'' T^2$ and that of the Sun must be less than $+2\cdot4'' T^2$. He concludes from these eclipses that the secular acceleration of the Moon lies between $+11\cdot0'' T^2$ and $+10\cdot3'' T^2$ and that of the Sun between $1\cdot6'' T^2$ and $1\cdot2'' T^2$. Combining these results with those he had previously obtained from a discussion of lunar eclipses, occultations, and equinoxes, he gives as his final values:

Secular acceleration of the Moon $= +10\cdot8'' T^2$

,,   ,,   ,,   Sun $= +1\cdot5'' T^2$

where T is expressed in centuries.

From a study of ancient occultations and eclipses, and the solar eclipses of $+1239$ June 3 and $+1715$ May 3, Schoch† has obtained results in fair accordance with Fotheringham. He finds for the secular accelerations of Sun and Moon the values $+2\cdot60'' T^2$ and $12\cdot20'' T^2$.

Fotheringham's most recent contribution‡ to this subject takes the form of a discussion of two eclipses only. The element which is most difficult to identify in an ancient eclipse is the time at which it occurred, on account of the inaccuracy with which time was described by the ancients: but as ancient horology was based on a time-interval after sunrise or sunset, it is possible to fix the time with some accuracy if it is stated that the eclipse occurred shortly before or after sunrise or sunset. Thus a total eclipse of the sun took place on -321 September 16 at Sippara beginning $4U\check{S}$ before sunset, the Babylonian $U\check{S}$ being four minutes; again, an eclipse of the Moon took place on -424 October 9 beginning $10U\check{S}$ after sunset at Nippur. The times of these eclipses are established with a possible error of only a few minutes. From this material alone Fotheringham obtained a value $+9\cdot5'' T^2$ for the difference between the accelerations of the Moon and the Sun. The mean of Fotheringham and Schoch is $11\cdot0'' T^2$ for the Moon and $2\cdot0'' T^2$ for the Sun.

Tidal Friction in the Irish Sea. There remains a difference of about $+4\cdot5'' T^2$ in the secular acceleration of the Moon and $+2\cdot0'' T^2$ in that of the Sun to be accounted for. It has been generally assumed that the former might be accounted for by the friction of the tides. Taylor‖ showed that this friction in the Irish Sea was much greater

† *Die säkulare acceleration des Mondes und der Sonne* (1926). Reprinted as supplement to *Astronomische Nachrichten*, Band 9, No. 2 (1830).

‡ *M.N.R.A.S.* **95**, 719 (1935).   ‖ *Phil. Trans.*, Series A, **220**, 1 (1920).

than had previously been calculated on the supposition that it resulted from the sliding of horizontal layers of water over one another. He gives reasons for showing that the formula $F = 0{\cdot}002\rho V^2$, where F is the friction, V the velocity of the current, and ρ the density of the water, which he had previously found for the friction of the wind on the ground, was applicable to tidal currents. A similar formula is used by engineers for the friction in large rivers. The dissipation of energy given by the tidal currents of the Irish Sea, which have an average velocity of $2\frac{1}{4}$ knots or 114 cm. per sec., calculated in this way amounts to 1,300 ergs per sq. cm. per sec.

Taylor verified this result by calculation of the rate at which energy enters the Irish Sea by the south and north channels and subtracting the work done by the lunar attraction, and finds a dissipation of energy of 1,530 ergs per sq. cm. per sec. Over the whole area of the Irish Sea the dissipation of energy is $2{\cdot}5 \times 10^{17}$ ergs per sec. or $3{\cdot}0 \times 10^{17}$ ergs per sec. according to these two estimates. In collaboration with Taylor's work Jeffreys[†] calculated the dissipation of energy necessary to produce a secular acceleration in the Moon's longitude of 4·5″ per century as $1{\cdot}41 \times 10^{19}$ ergs, and on this assumption 1/56th of the total dissipation is caused by the Irish Sea.

Jeffreys considers the effect of the Sun as well as the Moon. He finds that these are in the ratio of 1 : 3·4. Thus the effect of the Sun is much greater than would be supposed on the theory of bodily friction.

This ratio agrees well with Fotheringham's determination of 1·5 and 4·8 for the hitherto unaccounted for secular variations indicated by ancient observations. There can be little doubt that dissipation of energy by the tides is amply sufficient to account for these secular accelerations. At first sight it would seem that the Irish Sea contributes too large a proportion, but it is to be remembered that the dissipation of energy varies as the cube of the velocity, so that strong currents and shallow seas are the contributing factors, and the open oceans contribute practically nothing to the total dissipation. Jeffreys[‡] has examined the areas where dissipation in the semi-diurnal lunar tide is most likely to occur. He finds

$2{\cdot}4 \times 10^{18}$ in European waters,

$2{\cdot}6 \times 10^{18}$ in Asiatic waters,

$2{\cdot}0 \times 10^{18}$ in American waters,

and $15{\cdot}0 \times 10^{18}$ in the Bering Sea.

† *M.N.R.A.S.* **80**, 308 (1920).   ‡ *Phil. Trans.* **221**, 239 (1921).

This gives a total of $2\cdot 2 \times 10^{19}$ ergs per sec., which is greater than $1\cdot 4 \times 10^{19}$ ergs per sec. required to account for the secular acceleration of the Moon. There is reason for supposing that the amount of dissipation may have been over-estimated owing to insufficient data to as much as twice its amount.

VII

THE DEFLEXION OF LIGHT BY THE SUN'S GRAVITATIONAL FIELD

THE possibility that light and matter might be convertible is suggested in Newton's *Optics*, Query 30. That a beam of light exerts pressure was pointed out by Maxwell and experimentally verified by Lebedew and by Nichols and Hull.

In 1911 Einstein showed that, a beam of light being subject to gravitation like a material particle in Newtonian dynamics, the deflexion of the light of a star passing near the Sun would be $0.87''a/r$, where a is the radius of the Sun and r the distance of the star from the Sun's centre. This is readily proved as follows.

The deflexion is the angle between the asymptotes, which in a hyperbola of great eccentricity is $2/e$. The velocity at the nearest point to the Sun is c the velocity of light. If G is the constant of gravitation and M the mass of the Sun, h twice the area described in unit time, and l the latus rectum of the hyperbola,

$$h^2 = GM.l,$$

or

$$c^2 r^2 = GMer.$$

Thus

$$GM = c^2 r/e.$$

If d be the Earth's mean distance and v its mean velocity

$$GM = v^2 d.$$

Thus

$$\frac{2}{e} = 2\frac{v^2}{c^2}\frac{d}{r}.$$

If a be radius of Sun, $d = 215a$ and v/c is the aberration constant $= 20.47''$.

Thus

$$\frac{2}{e} = 2 \times 215 \times (20.47)^2 \sin 1'' \frac{a}{r}$$

$$= 0.87'' \frac{a}{r}.$$

Freundlich examined a number of photographs taken at previous eclipses, but was unable to obtain any result as the photographs were on too small a scale or contained too few stars.

An attempt to verify this deflexion was made at the Russian

eclipse by Campbell and Curtiss in 1914, but weather conditions were unfavourable and no result was obtained.

In 1915 Einstein brought out the General Theory of Relativity. According to this theory the deflexion by a gravitational field is twice the amount given by the Newtonian dynamics, namely $1.75''a/r$. For the proof of this, reference should be made to works on relativity.

The Lick Observatory attacked this difficult problem at the eclipse of 1918. Campbell,[†] as a result of a preliminary discussion, stated that the photographs did not show the full displacement and probably not the half amount. As no final discussion was published, presumably the conclusion was reached that the results were unreliable.

British Expeditions. Two expeditions[‡] were arranged by the British Eclipse Committee in November 1917 to observe the eclipse of 1919 May 29, as the field of stars was very favourable for the purpose. After the conclusion of the War the instruments were assembled at Greenwich, and arrangements made with all speed for the observers to leave England on March 8, 1919. Eddington and Cottingham took an astrographic object-glass lent by Turner and a 16-inch coelostat to Principe on the coast of Africa. Davidson and Crommelin took an astrographic object-glass with a 16-inch coelostat and a 4-inch object-glass of 19-feet focus with an 8-inch coelostat to Sobral in north Brazil. Steel tubes were constructed for the two astrographic object-glasses. The 4-inch telescope had the wooden tube used by Father Cortie in 1914, but modified somewhat to give greater rigidity and constancy of focus.

The coordinates of the observed stars and their photographic magnitudes are

		m.	x	y
2	Pi. iv. 82	5·8	$+54'$	$-16'$
3	κ^2 Tauri	5·5	$+18$	$+18$
4	κ^1 Tauri	4·5	$+17$	$+24$
5	Pi. iv. 61	6·0	-8	-55
6	v Tauri	4·5	$+29$	$+55$
10	72 Tauri	5·5	$+43$	$+66$
11	66 Tauri	5·5	-63	-8
Sun at Principe			$+28$	-12
Sun at Sobral			$+22$	-13

† *Observatory*, **42**, 298 (1919). *P.A.S.P.* **35**, 11 (1923).

‡ *Phil. Trans.*, Series A, **220**, 291 (1920). *Smithsonian Report for 1919*, p. 133 (1921).

At Principe the sky was clouded, but two plates were obtained showing images of the stars 5, 4, 3, 6, 10 and 11, 4, 3, 6, 10 respectively. Check fields were obtained the same night, and as the temperature was the same by night and day, it was assumed that there was no change of scale. Plates for comparison of the eclipse field and the check field had been taken previously at Oxford by Bellamy before the instrument was dismounted. Corrections for differential refraction and aberration were applied to all the measures. The measures were made at Cambridge by Eddington, an Oxford and Principe plate being placed film to film. In this way the images were nearly coincident, as the coelostat mirror gave a reflection of the field. Comparison of each of the two plates was made with two Oxford plates, and the final result of 1·65″ was in good agreement with Einstein's predicted value.

At Sobral the observers were favoured with fine weather, and obtained seven photographs with each of the two instruments, showing the seven stars given above. The images with the 4-inch lens of 19 feet focal length were in excellent focus, all being round except 11, which shows a slight elongation owing to its distance from the centre of the field. The photographs taken with the astrographic telescope were not satisfactory. Davidson noted 'May 30, 3 a.m., four of the astrographic plates were developed and when dry examined. It was found that there had been a serious change in focus so that, while the stars were shown, the definition was spoilt. This change of focus can only be attributed to the unequal expansion of the mirror through the Sun's heat. The readings of the focussing scale were checked next day but were found unaltered at 11·0 mm. It seems doubtful whether much can be got from these plates.' The observers stayed in Brazil and took photographs of the field on July 13, 14, 16, 17 at as near the same altitude as possible on those dates. Photographs were also taken through the glass to facilitate the measurement, as the eclipse and comparison plates could be placed film to film, so that the images were close together in the micrometer.

The measures were reduced for each eclipse and comparison plate separately. In the first instance, separate plate constants (Turner's method) were computed with an additional term for the Einstein deflexion for the right ascensions and declinations. From the right ascensions a value 2·06″ was found, and from the declinations 1·94″, and giving double weight to the declinations a deflexion of 1·98″ as compared with Einstein's 1·75″ was obtained. The values of the linear terms in the refraction and aberration were next computed for each plate and the normal equations combined and re-solved on the supposition that the value of the scale correction was the same in both directions and the orientation taken as the mean of the determinations in right ascension and declination. The mean of the plates gave the following table for the displacement of each star as compared with the theoretical value.

No. of star	Displacement in R.A.		Displacement in Decl.		Observed − Predicted	
	Observed	Predicted	Observed	Predicted		
	″	″	″	″	″	″
11	−0·19	−0·32	+0·16	+0·02	+0·13	+0·14
5	−0·29	−0·31	−0·46	−0·43	+0·02	−0·03
4	−0·11	−0·10	+0·83	+0·74	−0·01	+0·09
3	−0·20	−0·12	+1·00	+0·87	−0·08	+0·13
6	−0·10	+0·04	+0·57	+0·40	−0·14	+0·17
10	−0·08	+0·09	+0·35	+0·32	−0·17	+0·03
2	+0·96	+0·85	−0·27	−0·09	+0·11	−0·18

The authors had no hesitation in regarding the observations in Principe and Sobral as verifying Einstein's prediction of a deflexion of 1·75″ at the Sun's limb. The plates taken with the astrographic object-glass at Sobral were measured and the results published, but no weight was attached to them on account of the observer's note at the time.

The importance of the result naturally evoked criticism of the observations. The only one of any importance by Russell† had reference to the apparent distortion indicated by differences in the scale −0·146″ and orientation −0·250″ obtained from the right ascensions and declinations respectively. He showed that this distortion was a contraction of 0·26″ in the direction of the vertical, and suggested as a possible explanation a distortion of the coelostat mirror owing to the heat of the Sun. This, however, would not be a spherical distortion, but of a cylindrical character. The excellence of the images, although not absolute proof, is strongly against this.

Rediscussion of the Observations. With Davidson, we have rediscussed the published measures. After correcting the refraction for second-order terms as well as those of first order and for aberra-

† *M.N.R.A.S.* **81**, 155 (1920).

tion, determinations are given for the deflexion, scale value, and orientation in directions approximately 30° apart.

	Direction	Defl.	Scale	Orienta-tion	Rel. weights		
		"	"	"			
Horizontal .	0°	1·98	0·476	0·190	2·39	1·43	4·70
(Declination) .	+28° 48′	1·95	0·396	0·093	2·22	1·98	2·98
.. ..	+57° 36′	1·92	0·273	0·117	1·61	2·45	2·30
Vertical . .	90°	2·12	0·161	0·127	1·09	1·67	2·22
(Right Ascension)	+118° 48′	2·01	0·293	0·343	1·24	1·20	1·90
.. ..	+147° 36′	1·99	0·422	0·323	1·85	1·17	5·09

The values of scale and orientation have ranges of 0·32″ and 0·25″ at 50′ from the centre, but the value of the deflexion is more consistent. Although there seems to be a distortion of the field, *possibly*† *arising from a stratification of the air in the telescope*, it does not seem materially to have affected the amount of the deflexion, and the value of 1·98″ as given indicates that the deflexion is 1·75″ at least and possibly somewhat larger.

The radial displacements of the individual stars compared with the predicted displacements are given below.

Star	Calculation	Observation
	"	"
3	0·88	1·02
2	0·85	0·97
4	0·75	0·84
5	0·53	0·54
6	0·40	0·56
10	0·33	0·32
11	0·32	0·20

The next opportunity of verifying the deflexion of light occurred at the eclipse of 1922 September 21. Spencer Jones and Melotte took a complete equatorial mounting of the Greenwich astrographic telescope—suitably altered for latitude—to Christmas Island, and proposed to give exposures on the eclipse field and, by moving the telescope in declination, to a suitable comparison field during the eclipse. The intention was to determine the scale value from the latter plate, and by comparison with plates of the two fields taken at Greenwich to avoid the diminution of weight when scale and deflexion are obtained from the same plate. Unfortunately, the sky was completely cloudy at the time of the eclipse.

† It may be noted that the astrographic plates which were rejected were in a closed metal tube.

Lick Observatory Expedition. The expedition of Campbell and Trumpler† to Wallal on the north-west coast-line of Australia was completely successful. They used two lenses of 5 inches aperture and 15 feet focal length, covering so large a field that plates 17 inches square were required. The mounting was equatorial. Comparison plates of the eclipse field were taken at Tahiti in May some months before the eclipse, and a check field 90° distant in right ascension and at the same declination was also photographed. At Wallal the check field was photographed on the evening before the eclipse and the plate left in the carrier so that the eclipse field was photographed on the same plate. An exposure of two minutes was given, and after a short interval a second plate on which the check field had been taken was also exposed. The check field was used to determine the two square terms necessary to allow for the change in the inclination of the optical axis, but were not used for the determination of scale. The four plates were first reduced by the use of six constants. These are not given, but the agreement of scale and orientation was found to be satisfactory for the two plates taken with one of the lenses, and reasons are given why six constants were used for the plates taken with the second lens.

There were many more stars, but not so near the Sun as in the field of 1919. No less than 118 stars were photographed. Weights are assigned to separate stars from 3·9 for the brighter stars to 0·22 for the fainter stars. There are only 28 stars for which the weight is less than 1·0. The measures of the stars to which a weight greater than 3 is given are shown on p. 49.

The mean result from the four plates, which are in satisfactory accordance, is 1·72″, corresponding to Einstein's predicted value of 1·75″. Reasons are given for not comparing with the check stars, which would have increased the deflexion to 2·05″. There can be no doubt that the observations show a deflexion as great as and possibly rather more than Einstein's predicted value.

Freundlich's Expedition. Professor Freundlich, who had bad luck in the eclipses of 1914, 1921, 1922, and 1926, had better fortune at the eclipse of 1929 May 9 in north Sumatra. He had two instruments. The first consisted of two cameras of 28 feet focal length and 5-inch object-glasses with fields of 3°×3°. These both faced a 30-inch coelostat mirror, and were set at 25° in azimuth, the one

† *L.O.B.* 346 (1923).

No.	Phot. Mag.	Distance	Δx	Δy	Rad. Comp.	Theory†
	m.	° ′	″	″	″	″
63	7·3	0 33	+0·24	+0·68	+0·72	+0·81
78	8·4	0 57	+0·49	+0·09	+0·49	+0·43
81	7·5	1 7	+0·37	+0·07	+0·32	+0·34
59	8·3	1 8	+0·07	−0·35	+0·36	+0·33
37	9·7	1 29	−0·23	+0·29	+0·37	+0·22
51	9·4	1 36	+0·08	−0·21	+0·20	+0·18
25	6·9	1 40	−0·12	−0·14	+0·11	+0·17
64	9·1	1 43	+0·15	+0·15	+0·17	+0·16
86	8·0	1 44	+0·04	−0·16	−0·09	+0·16
102	8·2	1 54	+0·24	+0·06	+0·21	+0·13
104	9·3	1 56	−0·06	−0·06	−0·06	+0·12
98	9·3	1 58	+0·42	−0·15	+0·44	+0·11
99	9·0	1 58	+0·29	+0·11	+0·20	+0·11
58	8·4	2 2	+0·26	−0·18	+0·19	+0·10
28	8·2	2 4	−0·12	+0·01	+0·08	+0·10
68	8·8	2 5	+0·16	−0·16	+0·19	+0·10
105	8·8	2 5	+0·12	−0·04	+0·13	+0·10
110‡	7·8	2 34	−0·64	−0·21	−0·67	+0·02
5	8·3	2 38	+0·02	−0·04	+0·02	+0·01
89	8·3	2 47	+0·16	+0·29	−0·19	−0·01
96	7·8	2 51	+0·13	+0·08	+0·01	−0·02

pointing on the eclipsed Sun and the second on a check field. Comparison photographs of the eclipse and check field were taken some months later. In addition a *réseau* from a collimating telescope was printed on the four series of plates. This was satisfactory as far as the eclipse and its comparison field was concerned, but not as regards the check fields, as the lines were distorted. It was, therefore, not possible to verify from the check fields whether there had been any change of scale. The field of stars was not very favourable, as nearly all lay on the east side of the Sun. The nearest star was only 8′ from the Sun's limb. The resulting value for the displacement at the Sun's limb was found to be 2·2″. The table on the next page is taken from the discussion of the results in the *Zeitschrift für Astrophysik*, vol. **3**, but rearranged according to distance from the Sun's centre. The result was criticized by Trumpler‖ and by Jackson†† on the ground that the scale of the *réseau* had changed. Trumpler, on this assumption, finds by re-reduction the value 1·75″.

The second instrument mounted equatorially had a focal length of 11 ft. 3 in. and had a large field of $7·5° \times 7·5°$. The camera was first

† A small-scale correction is applied to the Einstein displacement to make the figures strictly comparable with the preceding column.

‡ Large residual possibly due to nearness to edge of plate.

‖ *P.A.S.P.* **44**, 167 (1932).   †† *Observatory*, **54**, 292 (1931).

Distance from centre, in units of Sun's radius	Observed radial displacement	Value 1·75″ a/r	Observed — calculated	Inclination to radius
			″	°
1·52	+1·30	+1·15	+0·15	+17
2·42	+0·78	+0·78	+0·00	+ 2
2·62	+0·74	+0·67	+0·07	+17
2·76	+0·83	+0·63	+0·20	− 9
2·76	+0·75	+0·63	+0·12	− 4
2·86	+0·88	+0·61	+0·27	+10
3·20	+0·73	+0·55	+0·18	+ 7
3·25	+0·84	+0·54	+0·30	+10
3·53	+0·78	+0·49	+0·29	+ 6
4·04	+0·48	+0·43	+0·05	+ 8
4·21	+0·54	+0·41	+0·13	+21
4·42	+0·42	+0·39	+0·03	− 1
5·06	+0·70	+0·34	+0·36	− 3
5·08	+0·50	+0·34	+0·16	+ 9
5·89	+0·51	+0·30	+0·21	−17
5·89	+0·60	+0·30	+0·30	+ 2
6·42	+0·26	+0·27	−0·01	+34
7·54	+0·42	+0·23	+0·19	−26

pointed on the field of the Sun and then on a field sufficiently distant to have no appreciable Einstein displacement. The observations are discussed in the *Annalen v.d. Bosscha-Sterrewacht*, Lembang, Java, and it is stated that satisfactory results are not obtainable by this method.

Other results, but of smaller weight, are obtained by Trumpler with a telescope of 5 feet focal length giving 1·82″; by Chant and Young (focal length 10 ft.) giving 1·74″; and by Dodwell and Davidson (focal length 5 ft.) giving 1·77″.

The conclusion is that the displacement is at least as great as 1·75″, and possibly a little greater but not more than 2·0″. Possibly a slight excess over 1·75″ may be attributed to atmospheric causes. But there can be no doubt that Einstein's prediction has been verified. It is unquestionably very difficult to obtain the exact value by observation. Whether the scale value can be determined by pointing on a field 10° or more from the Sun during the eclipse is still an open question, as otherwise in the most favourable circum-stances the weight of the result is halved by the necessity for determining the scale from the same plates. But a good field of stars of 2° to 3° surrounding the Sun is a *sine qua non*, with a number of them sufficiently near the Sun's limb. Possibly plates sensitive in the red will enable stars to be photographed which would otherwise be drowned in the Corona.

VIII

ECLIPSES IN RELATION TO THE PHYSICAL STATE OF THE SUN FROM 1836 TO 1889

Early Visual Observations. Very little attention was paid by astronomers to the striking features of total eclipses—the Corona and the prominences—till nearly the middle of the nineteenth century. Agnes Clerke† gives an interesting account of the views of earlier astronomers, who were undecided whether the Corona arose from the Earth's atmosphere, or whether it belonged to an atmosphere of the Sun or Moon. That the Corona was in the immediate vicinity of the Sun was not admitted—strange as it may seem—by all astronomers till the advent of photography. Doubt was even thrown on the solar nature of the prominences till Secchi and de la Rue in 1860 showed that the Moon passed in front of them.

In 1836 Francis Baily observed an annular eclipse at Jedburgh in Scotland and drew attention to a picturesque feature which frequently occurs at the beginning and end of totality. 'When the Cusps of the Sun were about 40° asunder, a row of lucid points like a string of bright beads, irregular in size and distance from each other, *suddenly* formed round that part of the Moon which was about to enter or which might be considered as just having entered on the Sun's disc.' The aptness of this description has been recognized by the name 'Baily's beads' being given to this phenomenon. The correct explanation was given by Baily; the beads are due to irradiation on the irregular surface of the Moon.

An equally picturesque phenomenon is sometimes seen when at the commencement or end of totality a bright point of light similar to an electric lamp heralds the beginning of the eclipse or, more effectively, its conclusion.

Corona and Prominences. In 1842 the practice of making regular expeditions to observe total eclipses seems to have commenced. The expeditions of this year were plentifully rewarded with a magnificent view of Corona and prominences. The word Corona was first used in its present astronomical sense by Baily in describing this eclipse, though it was employed long ago by Seneca for the

† *History of Astronomy in the Nineteenth Century*, pp. 73–86.

haloes round the Sun due to atmospheric causes. Baily, observing at Pavia, writes:

'The dark body of the Moon was suddenly surrounded with a Corona or kind of bright glory similar in shape and relative magnitude to that which painters draw round the head of Saints and called by the French an *aureole.* . . . The breadth of the Corona measured from the circumference of the Moon appeared to me to be nearly half the Moon's diameter. The light was most dense close to the border of the Moon and became gradually and uniformly more attenuate as its distance therefrom increased, assuming the form of diverging rays, which at the extremity were more divided, and of an unequal length; so that in no part of the Corona could I discover the regular and well-defined shape of a ring at its *outer* margin. It appeared to me to have the Sun in its centre, but I had no means of taking any accurate measures for determining this point. Its colour was quite white, not pearl colour nor yellow nor red, and the rays had a vivid and flickering appearance. . . . But the most remarkable circumstance attending the phenomenon was the appearance of *three large protuberances* apparently emanating from the circumference of the Moon, but evidently forming a part of the Corona. They had the appearance of mountains of prodigious elevation; their colour was red tinged with lilac or purple, very different from the brilliant white light that formed the Corona. . . . The whole of these three protuberances were visible till the last moment of total obscuration.'

Airy described the Prominences as resembling saw-teeth, while Arago estimated their height at 2 minutes of arc—or 54,000 miles if they are on the Sun. The Corona was seen under excellent atmospheric conditions by Struve, who estimated its breadth as 25', while streamers were seen extending to 3 or 4 degrees from the Moon's limb. At this eclipse the general verdict of astronomers was that the Corona was not sufficiently bright to cast a shadow. On account of scattered sunlight it is generally impossible to compare the total light of the Corona with the full Moon. Attempts were made to compare the brightness of the Corona with that of a candle, and to compare this with that of the full Moon when at the same altitude at this and subsequent eclipses, but the results are extremely doubtful.

The eclipse of 1851 July 28 was well observed in Norway. A remarkable hook-shaped prominence was observed, and the Corona seen to a distance of about half the Moon's diameter. The view that the chromosphere was a continuous solar atmosphere was gradually received. The first astronomical photograph—a daguerreotype by Barkowski—was taken at Königsberg at this eclipse.

The First Photographic and Spectroscopic Observations. The collodion wet plate was invented in 1851. This required an exposure of only one-thirtieth of the daguerreotype process. At the eclipse of 1860 July 18 Warren de la Rue and Father Secchi obtained successful photographs at two stations in Spain 250 miles apart which agreed closely in the details of the prominences. Their photographs showed that the prominences were solar appendages as the Moon passed in front of them in the course of the eclipse.

At this eclipse definite evidence was obtained by Prazmowski of the radial polarization of the Corona, indicating that the light of the Corona consists in part of sunlight reflected from small particles. Successful photographs which served as a basis for a drawing of the Corona were taken by Whipple at Shellyville, Kentucky.

Spectroscopy was first applied to observations of eclipses in 1868 at the eclipse which passed over India and Malaya on August 18. Tennant, Janssen, Pogson, and Rayet all observed that the prominences gave a spectrum of bright lines. The red and blue lines were readily identified as hydrogen, and the yellow one was attributed to sodium. Later it was found by Lockyer that this line was not due to sodium, and was not emitted in the spectrum of any element then known. He supposed that the line was due to an unknown element existing in the Sun, but not yet isolated on earth, to which he gave the name helium. As is well known, a gas which was isolated in 1895 by Ramsay exhibits this line in its spectrum, and was at once identified with Lockyer's helium.

At the same eclipse Janssen was inspired by the sight of the prominences to see them in full daylight, and next day achieved his resolve, and watched their changing forms on subsequent days. By using sufficient dispersion he was able to reduce the atmospheric glare to such an extent that the bright red line emitted from the prominence showed its form in a widened slit placed tangential to the Sun's limb. Meanwhile Lockyer, on October 20, working independently on the same lines in London, achieved the same result. Lockyer's and Janssen's communications reached the Paris Academy of Sciences on the same day, and these two investigators were awarded a joint medal for their great discovery.

The eclipse of 1869 August 7 was visible in the United States, and

Professor Harkness obtained a continuous spectrum of the Corona with one bright line in the green. The position of this line was (wrongly) identified by Young with a dark line due to iron and called K 1474 from its number in Kirchhoff's solar spectrum, having a wave-length 5316·0 A.

Observations from 1870 to 1875. The eclipse of 1870 December 22, which was visible in Spain, North Africa, Greece, and Turkey, was remarkable for the discovery of 'the reversing layer' or 'flash spectrum' as it has been variously called. Young, placing the slit of his spectroscope tangential to the Sun near the moment of totality, saw the dark-line solar spectrum gradually fade away and suddenly become replaced by bright lines. It gave to him the impression of a complete reversal of the Fraunhofer spectrum. He identified about 20 lines, including the hydrogen lines Hα and Hβ, the sodium and magnesium lines, and the line D 3 (5875·6 A.) of helium. He also examined carefully the green Coronal line, and found that its wave-length agreed with his determination in 1869 and that the line extended to a distance of 16′ from the Sun's limb, though he was doubtful of the reality of this extension. Young carefully examined the spectrum of the Corona for dark lines, but found none. Observations of polarization were made by several astronomers. Langley found evidences of this to a distance of 40′ from the limb. Blaserna found radial polarization to a distance of 30′ but no farther.

At the eclipse of 1871 December 12, which passed over southern India, photographs of the Corona showed a considerable advance on those taken in former years, and exhibited the forms of the streamers and the tufts at the north and south pole. In this eclipse Respighi and Lockyer placed a prism in front of the object-glass of the telescope instead of using a slit spectroscope, and obtained bright arcs of the chromosphere at the beginning and end of the eclipse. Respighi made visual observations of these, while Lockyer obtained photographs. They identified the four hydrogen lines Hα, Hβ, Hγ, Hδ and the Coronal line K 1474.

Janssen, who placed the slit of his spectroscope 12′ from the limb, found these bright lines, and also the dark D line and another dark line which he could not identify. The importance of this observation is its confirmation of the polariscopic result, showing that the light of the Corona is partly reflected sunlight.

The eclipse of 1874 April 16 was observed by Stone in South Africa.

The Corona had long streamers said to extend to three degrees from the Sun's centre. At the moment of totality a large number of bright lines were seen, giving the impression of a reversal of the Fraunhofer spectrum. The line K 1474 and no others were seen when the Corona was examined at some distance from the limb.

For the eclipse of 1875 April 6, which passed over Siam, Lockyer proposed that an attempt should be made to photograph the spectrum of the Corona. As he was himself unable to leave England, the expedition was put in charge of Schuster. No spectrum of the Corona was obtained. The existence of the H and K lines of calcium in the prominences was detected, though the dispersion was insufficient to separate the two lines. The form of the Corona was very similar to that of the previous year.

Observations from 1878 to 1889. The eclipse of 1878 July 19 was observed by many astronomers in the United States of America. From the summit of Pike's Peak Langley† observed streamers extending to as much as 6°, the longest being in the ecliptic. This naturally suggested a connexion with the zodiacal light. The polar tufts were well shown with their suggestion of lines of force round a bar magnet. The intensity of the chromospheric spectrum and of the Coronal line K 1474 were comparatively small.

The eclipse of 1882 May 17 was well observed in Egypt. The Corona was like that of 1871, eleven years previously, when the sunspots were near their maximum. This confirmed previous views of the relationship of the form of the Corona with the activity of the Sun shown by its spots. With dry plates, which were now in use, excellent photographs of the Corona were taken by Schuster.‡ A number of chromospheric lines were obtained by him with a slit spectroscope, while the H and K lines and a long series of hydrogen lines were found by Lockyer‖ in a prominence photographed by a prismatic camera.

The eclipse of 1883 May 6, being of very long duration, was observed in the Caroline Islands by many astronomers from Europe and America. Photographs were taken showing the Corona very clearly. The most important observation was the confirmation of the presence of dark Fraunhofer lines in the spectrum of the Corona by Janssen.††

† *Washington Observations*, 1876, p. 209.   ‡ *Proc. R.S.* **35**, 151 (1883).
‖ Abney, *Phil. Trans.* **175**, 267 (1884).   †† *C.R.* **97**, 592 (1883).

The eclipses of 1886, 1887, and 1889 yielded little advance except gradual improvement in the photography of the Corona, the small-scale photographs of Barnard of the eclipse of 1889 January 1 taken in California being particularly good. As very great advances in eclipse spectroscopy were to be made at subsequent eclipses, a natural period, that of the pioneer stage in the photography of eclipse spectra, draws to a close with the eclipse of 1889.

Full details of the observations made at the total eclipses from 1836 to 1878 are collected by Ranyard in vol. **41** of the *Memoirs* of the Royal Astronomical Society, with references to the original publications.

ECLIPSE EXPEDITIONS—INSTRUMENTS

ORGANIZED expeditions to observe total solar eclipses have been made about fifty times. Predicted tracks of the central band are usually prepared several years in advance, and intending observers select stations in accordance as far as possible with railway and steamer facilities. Meteorological inquiries are made as to the probability of fine weather at the time of year and time of day at which the eclipse will occur. This probability has to be determined from the records of preceding years and is very far from certainty. The observers go hoping for the best and prepared for the worst.

Before the advent of photography the observers had only small telescopes, spectroscopes, or polariscopes. At the present time equipment is much more elaborate, and preparations are made for housing the instruments in temporary observatories which will provide shelter from rain and sun, as well as from wind and dust. Piers of concrete or brick have to be built for the instruments. A developing room for photographs is desirable, at any rate for preliminary observations for focussing, etc. When a comparison spectrum is required, provision has to be made for suitable electric current. Experience shows that it is as well to leave ample time to erect the instruments before the day of the eclipse.

Fall of Illumination and Temperature. The general fall of intensity of visual light is well shown by a diagram (Fig. 14) given by Stetson, Coblentz, Arnold, and Spurr[†] made in Sumatra at the eclipse of 1926 January 14 by means of a Macbeth illuminometer, which could be adjusted in various ways to give readings from 0·003 to 10,000 foot-candles.

The eclipse commenced at U.T. $6^h 10^m$, mid-eclipse was at $7^h 35^m 50^s$, and the total phase lasted $4·2^m$.

The fall in temperature is shown in the table on the next page.

Diminishing Crescent. The time of commencement of the total phase at a station whose longitude and latitude are known may be predicted correctly to 3 or 4 seconds. If, however, the longitude of the station is only imperfectly known, the time of commencement of the total phase, as judged by the observer's chronometer, may well

† *Ap. J.* **66**, 65 (1928).

be 10 seconds in error. As it is of importance to know the moment
of commencement of totality more nearly, the diminishing crescent

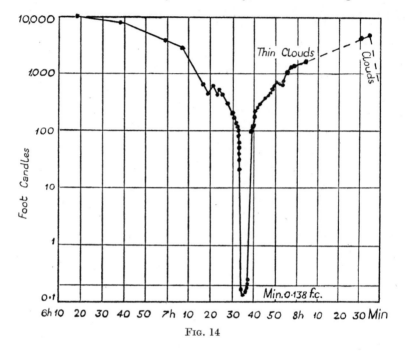

FIG. 14

	Thermometer	
Time	Wet-bulb	Dry-bulb
U.T. h. m.	°	°
6 46	78·4	88·1
56	78·0	86·2
7 06	78·1	85·6
16	76·0	83·8
35	76·0	82·0 (estimated)
8 03	76·1	82·5
14	76·1	83·6
26	78·0	85·6
35	77·2	86·1
43	79·3	86·8

of the Sun is watched on the ground-glass of the camera. For a
point of the central line let S be the centre of the Sun, M of the Moon,
and $ADBC$ the crescent, subtending an angle 2θ at S.

Let D be the radius of the Sun, $D+d$ that of the Moon, and $2T$ sec.
the duration of the total phase; and let $CD = d/n$.

Then
$$MS = d\left(1+\frac{1}{n}\right).$$

The equations of the two circles are
$$x^2+y^2 = D^2$$
$$\left\{x-d\left(1+\frac{1}{n}\right)\right\}^2+y^2 = (D+d)^2.$$

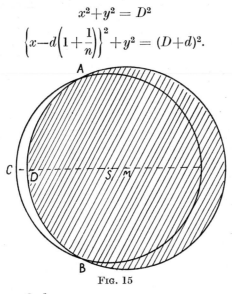

FIG. 15

Subtracting, we find
$$x = \frac{n}{n+1}D+\frac{2n+1}{n(n+1)}d,$$

or
$$\cos\theta = \frac{n}{n+1}+\frac{2n+1}{2n(n+1)}\frac{d}{D}.$$

d/D rarely exceeds $\frac{1}{16}$.

Putting $n = 1$, i.e. T sec. before second contact,
$$\cos\theta \text{ lies between } 0\cdot500 \text{ and } 0\cdot546,$$

or
$$\theta \text{ lies between } 60° \text{ and } 57°.$$

Omitting the term in d/D

For a total arc of 120° totality will follow in T sec.

,,	,,	90°	,,	,,	,,	0·41T sec.
,,	,,	60°	,,	,,	,,	0·155T sec.
,,	,,	30°	,,	,,	,,	0·035T sec.

If the observer is not on the central line, the time of the total phase $2T$ corresponds to a movement of the shadow through a distance $2d\sin\alpha$, where 2α is the angular distance between the points of second and third contact. At time T/n before second contact the semi-arc is given by the formula $\cos\theta = n/\sqrt{(n^2+2n\sin^2\alpha+\sin^2\alpha)}$. In this way the observer has sufficient warning to commence exposures for the flash spectrum or start the moving plate the right number of seconds before the total phase begins. At the moment of totality it is usual for seconds to be counted from a chronometer by a member of the party, so that exposures with different instruments may be begun and ended according to a specified programme.

The necessities imposed on eclipse observers by difficulties of transport and the brief time which can be spared for their erection have led to various expedients for simplifying the mounting.

Schaberle's Fixed Telescope. Schaberle[†] decided to obtain photographs on a larger scale than those observed hitherto at an eclipse he proposed to observe in Chile on April 16, 1893. He had at his disposal an excellent Clark objective of 5 inches aperture and 40 feet focal length. He decided not to use a horizontal telescope in connexion with a plane mirror driven by a heliostat, as he considered that the best results could not be obtained by using an intermediate reflecting surface, not to mention the rotation of the field in a long exposure. The transport and erection of an equatorial mounting was impracticable. He therefore decided to use a fixed telescope pointing at the Sun at the moment of the eclipse. The object-glass was mounted on one pillar, and a movable photographic plate on a second. The motion of the slide carrying the photographic plate was regulated by inclined guides and clockwork to give the velocity and direction of the Sun's image at the time of the eclipse. The tube of the telescope was of canvas painted black inside and outside, 2 feet square at the objective end, expanding to 4 feet at the eye end, and terminating in the dark room where the observer was stationed. The canvas tube was kept clear of the objective and the moving slides. Although in the course of the eclipse the Sun is sometimes at a distance from the optical axis, optical aberrations are inappreciable owing to the great focal length. Excellent photographs were taken at this eclipse, and a similar installation was employed by astronomers from the Lick Observatory in several later expeditions.

A still larger telescope was used by Miller and the Swarthmore College observers at the eclipses of 1918, 1923, 1925, and 1926. A 9-inch objective of focal length 63 feet was used, and a tower of 53 feet had to be built. The car carrying the photographic plate

† *L.O.*, No. 4.

PLATE 2

RESTRICTED EQUATORIAL MOUNTING AS USED BY CAMPBELL IN 1922

moved 3·09 inches a minute. Excellent photographs of the Corona with a Moon's image of seven inches were obtained.

Campbell's Polar Axis. If an equatorial mounting is used at an eclipse, it is not necessary that the telescope should be available as in an observatory for all parts of the sky. Provided an efficient driving can be secured for 20 minutes at the time of totality, other requirements are not essential. Campbell† at the Indian eclipse of 1898 used a polar axis which carried two spectrographs and three photographic telescopes. The polar axis was a strong plank box, 12 by 15 inches in section, 9 feet long, mounted parallel to the Earth's axis on steel pivots at each end, running in roller bearings. From the middle of one side of the box a strong arm thoroughly braced in every direction ran out ten feet, at right angles to the box. At the outer end of the arm a sector of 10-foot radius was fastened. An astronomical driving-clock securely mounted very close to the sector released a cord which pressed against the face of the sector, and lowered it at a uniform rate. The polar axis served as a packing-case. The same mounting was used successfully at Flint Island in 1908, and in Australia in 1922. The same method of driving was used on the 15-foot photographic telescope for the gravitational displacement predicted by Einstein, and furnished the most complete test of the accuracy of the driving. This method has been extensively used by American astronomers.

The Coelostat. A great convenience in eclipse observations is obtained by the use of reflecting mirrors. A telescope of any length can be used, and spectroscopes can be conveniently mounted as in a laboratory. The polar heliostat, besides giving a rotation of the field, is not very satisfactory at large hour angles. In 1895 Lippmann observed that a mirror turning about an axis in its plane and pointing to the pole moving with half the diurnal rotation would not only give an image of the Sun in a definite azimuth, but would also give no rotation of the field. The geometry is readily seen from Fig. 16, which is a projection on the plane of the Meridian.

> Z is the Zenith,
> P and P' the poles,
> E the east point,
> S_1 the position of the Sun at rising,
> O a point so that $EO = ES_1$,
> M the normal to the mirror.

† *P.A.S.P.* **10**, 131 (1898).

The Sun moves along the parallel to S_2. OS_2 is bisected at the Equator at M. O is the fixed direction of the ray reflected by a mirror whose normal is in direction M. As the angle $MS_2P = MOP'$, the north point of the Sun still remains the north point in the image. The point M moves with half the diurnal motion along the Equator.

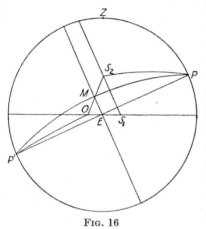

FIG. 16

There are two points at which the camera may be mounted horizontally, one suitable for an eclipse in the morning, as in the diagram, so that the angle of incidence of the Sun's ray on the mirror is always less than 45°. For an eclipse in the afternoon O would be in a similar relation to the setting-point of the Sun.

The mechanical construction is very simple, as the coelostat mirror rests in a cell clamped to the polar axis and moved by clockwork at half the diurnal rate. The adjustment of the polar axis is readily secured as in an equatorial, by obtaining the image of the Sun in the same position from observations in the early morning, near noon, and the evening.

Coelostats were constructed for the eclipse of 1896 on Turner's advice, and have been used by many observers in subsequent eclipses. The ease of movement and the adjustment to any required latitude are valuable features of this instrument. A slight disadvantage is that small changes must be made in the azimuth in consequence of the Sun's changing declination. The object-glass of the telescope is kept as near the coelostat mirror as possible, and provision should be made by previous calculation of the exact position of the camera end, as a change of several feet may occur in a long telescope between the time when the instrument was set up and the day of the eclipse. This can be avoided by use of a second mirror, but is not to be recommended for eclipse observations.

The difficulties which attend the use of coelostat mirrors are gradually being reduced. Silvering mirrors on the spot was sometimes necessary or spare mirrors had to be taken. Observers naturally protected the mirrors by exposing them as little as possible to direct

PLATE 3

COELOSTAT AND LONG-FOCUS CAMERA
(*Pacific and Atlantic Photos. Ltd.*)

sunlight to avoid alteration of figure. Probably aluminized mirrors of pyrex glass will be used in future expeditions.

The use of coelostat mirrors avoids the necessity for the erection of large towers and mechanism for moving the camera when large-scale photographs are required. They have also the advantage of allowing physical observations to be made as in a laboratory, where efficient temperature control can be made. Where slit spectroscopes are used, the prisms should be kept at constant temperature if the best results are to be obtained.†

The objection raised against them that the figure of the mirror is changed by the Sun's heat seems to us of little weight when sufficient care is taken by the observers to protect the mirror. The possibility of stratification in the horizontal telescope should be guarded against. A large open-work frame covered by canvas, shielded as much as possible from the Sun's heat, and provided with a fan for the circulation of the air should avoid this difficulty.

† See Carroll, *Nature*, Aug. 29, 1936, p. 351.

THE FLASH SPECTRUM

The Solar Spectrum at Second Contact. When Young† examined the solar spectrum visually at the eclipse of 1871 he saw that at the moment of second contact the weaker Fraunhofer lines reverse sharply from dark to bright. The bright lines appear to flash out sharply at second contact, and the emission spectrum at second (or third) contact is known as the flash spectrum. The strongest emission lines do not flash but remain visible for a longer interval: the whole emission spectrum is of course due to the topmost layers of the Sun's atmosphere which remain visible when the disk itself is cut off. The region is known as the chromosphere, the name having been given by Lockyer on account of its bright red appearance to the naked eye, and the region responsible for the flash spectrum is the lower chromosphere. The bright flash was at first thought to be an exact reversal of the Fraunhofer spectrum, and the layer responsible for it was called the reversing layer and presumed to be the seat of the formation of the Fraunhofer lines, but it is now known that the flash spectrum is far from being a reversal of the Fraunhofer spectrum.

In 1872, when Young made extensive observations on the spectrum of chromosphere and prominences, and made out a list of 273 lines in the visible spectrum, he concluded that they were for the most part reversals of the dark Fraunhofer lines. 'The selection of the lines', he remarks,‡ 'seems most capricious; one is taken and another left, though belonging to the same element, of equal intensity and close beside each other.' Subsequent eclipse expeditions extended and improved the observations. Lockyer took up the question in 1893 and sent two expeditions to observe the eclipse of that year, Fowler going to West Africa and Shackleton to Brazil, both of these observers securing photographs of the flash spectrum. Shackleton obtained better results in 1896 in Nova Zembla, but still more successful results were obtained in 1898 by Fowler and W. H. Lockyer in Lockyer's‖ expedition to India. Fowler operated a prismatic camera with a 6-inch aperture, focal length 90 inches, and two 45° prisms, while Lockyer's had an aperture

---

† *Mem. R.A.S.* **41**, 435.   ‡ *The Sun*, p. 206.
‖ *Phil. Trans.*, Series A, **197**, 151 (1901).

PLATE 4

FLASH SPECTRUM, 1898. (*Fowler*)

Labels on spectrum: 3933(K), {3968(H)}IONISED CALCIUM, 3970(Hε), 4102(Hδ), 4340(Hγ), 4471(Helium)

of 9 inches, focal length 120 inches, and one 45° prism. In order to ensure that the actual flash, which is of brief duration, should be photographed, each observer took ten snap exposures from 5 seconds before totality to 5 seconds after totality, changed plates for exposures on the spectrum of the Corona, and took ten more snapshots at third contact. These photographs were very successful, the 6-inch camera being in very sharp focus. The results of this expedition were not published until 1901, but were remarkable in that they were the first to demonstrate that the flash spectrum is not a reversal of the Fraunhofer spectrum.

Enhanced Lines in the Chromosphere. Observations at South Kensington had shown differences between the intensities of the lines in arc and spark spectra. Many weak lines in the arc appear greatly 'enhanced' in the spark: the differences were at first attributed to increased temperatures in the spark over the arc, but later a difference in the electrical conditions was considered to be a possible explanation of the differences in the spectra: the enhanced lines were attributed to a primitive state of the atom.

A large number of the 1898 chromospheric lines are identified as p.Ti (proto-titanium) and p.Fe and a smaller number as p.Cr, p.V, and p.Y, i.e. the enhanced lines of these elements. The carbon fluting at 3,883 A. is also shown. It was noted that the lines of H, He, Ca, and a line at 4,686 A.† reached to great heights. Altogether, 856 lines were measured and a fair proportion of them were identified. The presence of the helium lines, the extended series of hydrogen lines, and the increased intensity of the enhanced lines led to the conclusion that the chromospheric spectrum was 'not a mere reversal of the dark lines of ordinary sunlight into bright lines'. From the lengths of the arcs heights were found for many lines.

The same eclipse was observed by Evershed with much smaller apparatus: an object-glass of 2 inches and focal length of 36 inches with two crown-glass prisms in front of the object-glass. He obtained an extension in the ultra-violet as far as 3,342 A., obtained 30 lines of the Balmer series in good accordance with the formula, and drew attention to the continuous spectrum of the chromosphere and prominences beginning near the end of the series of hydrogen lines, which Huggins had found in the absorption spectra of early-type stars. Evershed deduced from his identifications that all the strong

† Since identified by Fowler as He+.

solar lines were found in the chromospheric spectrum, and that the relative intensities for any element were similar to those in the Fraunhofer spectrum but differed from one element to another, on account of the different heights to which they rise in the chromosphere. He concluded that the flash spectrum represented the upper and more extensively diffused portion of a stratum of gas which, by its absorption, gave the Fraunhofer dark-line spectrum.

The fact that the chromosphere did not present a mere reversal of the Fraunhofer lines was not accepted immediately. The 'enhanced' lines certainly presented a curious problem. The temperature of the chromosphere is necessarily less than the layer beneath, but the 'enhanced' lines apparently pointed to a higher temperature in the higher layer. Probably Lockyer was as much disturbed by this apparent anomaly as other astronomers, though one of the writers has heard him say, when questioned at the Royal Society, that in temperature he included electrical conditions. But to Lockyer and Fowler must be given the great credit of establishing by observation the enhanced lines as a characteristic of the chromospheric spectrum. Discussion of this question of the facts continued to flourish for several years, and other observers continued to assert that the chromospheric spectrum was a true reversal of the Fraunhofer spectrum, the relative intensities of enhanced and unenhanced lines being the same in the two cases.

Only preliminary results were given by Campbell,[†] Newall, and Hills. Newall[‡] noted that the absorption lines in the arcs near totality were of very different intensities from those in the usual Fraunhofer spectrum. Hills,[‡] who observed with two slit spectroscopes, gave the chromosphere from 3,930 A. to 4,340 A. side by side with the Fraunhofer spectrum in order to indicate the differences between them.

At the eclipse of 1900 May 28 the flash spectrum was observed in America by Campbell, Frost, Lord, and Mitchell, in Portugal by Dyson, and in North Africa by Newall and Evershed. Frost,[||] with a considerable dispersion, obtained 500 lines between 4,024 A. and 4,477 A. He concluded that the spectrum was essentially a reversal of the Fraunhofer spectrum and that there was no evidence of any relationship with the enhanced lines of Lockyer.

[†] *Ap. J.* **11**, 226 (1900).   [‡] *Proc. R.S.* **64**, 43 (1898).
[||] *Ap. J.* **12**, 307 (1900).

Lord,[†] on the other hand, whose spectra extended from 4,340 A. to 5,896 A., found considerable differences from the Fraunhofer spectrum. He noted that there were 73 lines of intensity 4 in Rowland's *Tables of the Solar Spectrum* which were not shown in his photographs, and that more than half of these were due to iron.

Evershed,[‡] who used a reflecting telescope and two light flint prisms, obtained excellent photographs of a higher dispersion than he had obtained in 1898. On account of a slight error in the predicted width of the track he was just outside the limit of totality, and in consequence the continuous spectrum was shown in his photographs, but bright arcs were shown with perfect clearness outside the continuous spectrum. His station was in such a position that the 'flash' spectrum was near the south pole of the Sun and was found to be the same as in equatorial regions. He obtained about 600 lines from 3,488 A. to 5,040 A., 300 of which were on the violet side of 4,000 A. Of the Balmer series, 30 lines were shown whose wave-lengths were in good accordance with the theoretical formula. In his discussion of these photographs he was decisive on the fact that the 'enhanced' lines play a significant part in the 'flash' spectrum, but held that as to the great majority of lines the chromospheric was a true reversal of the Fraunhofer spectrum.

The eclipse of 1901 May 18 was observed by many astronomers in Sumatra. Measures of lines in the spectra of the chromosphere were published at once by Humphreys and Mitchell. Humphreys,[||] with a 30-foot concave grating, obtained about 320 lines from 3,118 A. to 5,204 A. These observations of Humphreys were identified by Dewar with the lines of the rare gases of the atmosphere recently discovered, but this identification was soon shown to be erroneous by Lockyer. Mitchell[††] obtained 500 lines from 3,835 A. to 4,924 A., but saw no reason to give up his faith in the reversal of the Fraunhofer spectrum and failed to see the importance of the 'enhanced' lines.

Meanwhile, Fowler in June 1902[‡‡] pointed out that the 'enhanced' lines occurred in the spectrum of α Cygni, a giant star of type A2p in which the arc lines were not shown. Further, Lockyer and Baxendall[||||] showed that the relative intensities of spark and arc lines in γ Cygni,

---

† *Ap. J.* **13**, 149 (1901).   ‡ *Phil. Trans.*, Series A, **201**, 457 (1903).
|| *Ap. J.* **15**, 313 (1902).   †† *Ap. J.* **15**, 97 (1902).
‡‡ *Obs. Mag.* **25**, 233 (1902). |||| *Phil. Trans.* **201**, 205 (1903).

a giant star of type F8p, were very similar to those in the chromospheric spectrum, which, if anything, represented a slightly higher
temperature than that of the star.

At the eclipse of 1905 August 30 the chromospheric spectrum was
photographed by several astronomers. The results of photographs
taken in 1900, 1901, 1905, with slit spectroscopes, were published
by Dyson in 1906.† About 1,200 lines were shown extending from
3,300 A. to 5,875 A. Where the lines were identified they were
compared with the intensities in the solar, spark, and arc spectra.
The agreement with the spark spectra was much the best and
Lockyer's enhanced lines were prominently shown. The results entirely confirmed Lockyer's conclusion. It was noticed that the helium
lines were relatively strong in the higher chromosphere.

**Observations of the Chromospheric Spectrum without
Eclipse.** The observation of the chromospheric spectrum without an
eclipse had long been advocated by Hale, as it was impossible, on
account of the brief duration of the flash to photograph its spectrum
with a slit spectrograph of the highest dispersion. For this reason
slitless spectrographs, or prismatic cameras, were usually employed.
These record a great number of lines, but the absence of a slit prevents
one from measuring their wave-lengths with such precision as is
obtainable in other fields of solar research. These considerations
led Hale and Adams‡ to photograph the flash spectrum with high
dispersion in full sunlight. The practical difficulty arises that it is
necessary to keep the solar image accurately tangential to the slit
throughout the exposure. Preliminary results obtained in 1909 produced accurate wave-lengths for a limited number of lines including
the carbon band at 5,165 A. In 1914 Adams and Miss Burwell
published further results in which the spectrum from 4,800 A. to
6,600 A. was described as photographed with the 60-foot tower
telescope at Mount Wilson. The spectra were obtained in the second
order of the grating with exposures of 6 to 10 minutes, the scale being
0·9 A. per mm. The observation is only possible when the definition
is very good, which is rarely the case, but observations of this kind
are of the highest value. They refer to a low level in the chromosphere.

The chromospheric spectrum has also been photographed during
a partial eclipse. At the eclipse of 1912 April 17, when the obscura-

† *Phil. Trans.*, Series A, **206**, 403 (1906).
‡ *Ap. J.* **30**, 222 (1909).

tion was 0·9 of the solar disk in England, Newall[†] photographed between thirty and forty bright lines at Cambridge, while Fowler[‡] at South Kensington observed visually some hundreds of bright lines which persisted for half an hour round the time of mid-eclipse. Both observers were convinced that valuable results might be secured from observations of the cusps with a high resolving power. The same eclipse was observed in Spain, where the obscuration was 0·999, by Iniguez,[||] who observed 1,800 chromospheric lines between 3,334 A. and the D lines, confirming the intensification of enhanced lines in the chromospheric spectrum.

The Theoretical Problem presented by the Enhanced Lines. After 1905 no writer doubts the fact that the enhanced lines in the spectrum of the chromosphere are strengthened relative to the arc lines: the more accurate wave-lengths which were now obtained set aside all doubts on the question of observational fact, although the theoretical interpretation was to remain obscure for a further decade. Thus Mitchell,[††] writing as late as 1913 of his spectra obtained at the 1905 eclipse with good apparatus (he used a 4-inch parabolic grating giving 10·8 A. per mm. for the violet and a 6-inch Rowland grating giving 9·1 A. per mm. for the visible spectrum), finds that 'the chromospheric spectrum differs greatly from the solar spectrum in the intensities of the lines' and 'especially prominent in the chromospheric spectrum are the enhanced lines'. Writing of the enhanced lines in 1913, Mitchell says:

'The importance of enhanced lines in eclipse spectra was first recognized by Sir Norman Lockyer. The present measures confirm the important part played by the enhanced lines in the chromosphere, which are not only stronger but extend to higher levels than the unenhanced lines. . . . Lockyer's explanation of the brilliancy of the enhanced lines has always been one mainly of temperature. According to him, the spark is hotter than the arc, and at the higher temperature of the spark the element is dissociated. Applied to the chromosphere this bears the curious consequence that the higher levels are hotter than the lower, which seems a contradictory one.'

Mitchell quoted authorities to show that the spark was not necessarily hotter than the arc, and expressed the opinion that electrical conditions were responsible for the enhanced lines in both spark and

† *M.N.R.A.S.* **72**, 536 (1912).   ‡ *M.N.R.A.S.* **72**, 538 (1912).
|| *C.R.* **154**, 1142 (1912).   †† *Ap. J.* **38**, 407 (1913).

flash spectra. On the other hand, it must be remembered that Lockyer and Fowler had found enhanced lines in the spectra of stars which were hotter than the Sun; and as has been said before Lockyer had stated at the Royal Society that under temperature he included electrical conditions.

Ionization. It was not until 1920 that this problem received a satisfactory solution: it was clear that temperature could not be the only factor influencing the relative intensity of enhanced and arc lines, otherwise there would be no escape from the conclusion that the chromosphere was hotter than the reversing layer. The problem was the isolation of the unknown factor, which turned out to be pressure—more precisely the partial pressure of the electrons present. As early as 1913 Bohr showed from theoretical considerations alone that the Pickering series is due to ionized helium, or He^+, the series being as yet unknown in the laboratory, though it was immediately found by Fowler. Enhanced lines generally became identified with ionized elements; their occurrence in stellar spectra was attributed to dissociation of atoms into ions and electrons at the high temperature in the stellar atmospheres where enhanced lines occurred; but in 1920 Meg Nad Saha[†] made a vital advance, when he showed that, in addition to temperature, pressure influences a controlling influence on ionization, the reaction

$$Fe^+ + e \rightleftharpoons Fe$$

being similar to a reversible chemical reaction. At a given temperature and pressure the equilibrium between the three components—neutral iron atoms, ionized iron atoms, and electrons—is reached when the numbers of each per c.c. reach definite values. Increase of pressure increases the proportion of neutral to ionized atoms. Saha showed that the great ionization in the chromosphere is due to the very low pressure there, the decrease of pressure more than compensating for the drop in temperature from reversing layer to chromosphere. Hence the enhanced lines in the chromosphere. Pressure being taken into account, it seems only natural to expect a high degree of ionization in the outermost layers of the solar atmosphere, and it now requires an effort of historical imagination to appreciate the difficulties felt only twenty years ago.

Recent Chromospheric Spectra. At the eclipse of 1926 January 14 Davidson and Stratton[‡] photographed the spectrum of the chromo-

[†] *Phil. Mag.*, Oct. 1920.   [‡] *Mem. R.A.S.* **64**, 105.

PLATE 5

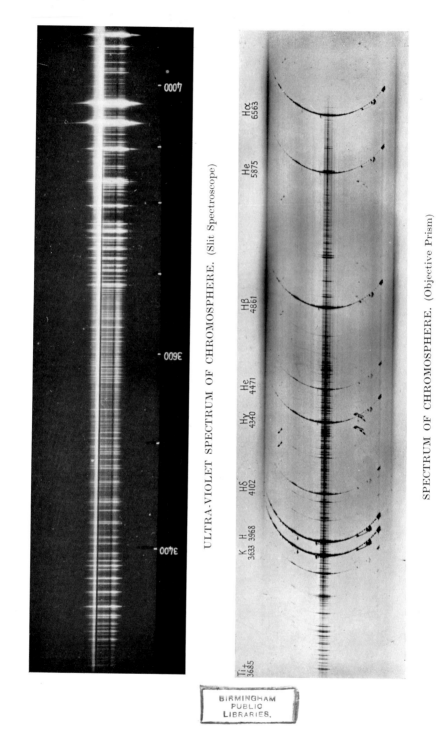

ULTRA-VIOLET SPECTRUM OF CHROMOSPHERE. (Slit Spectroscope)

SPECTRUM OF CHROMOSPHERE. (Objective Prism)

sphere, with the quartz spectrograph used by Hills in 1898 and by observers at later eclipses, between 3,066 A. and 4,216 A. Intensities on an arbitrary scale are given in the 'flash' and in a high prominence. They have identified the lines by direct comparison with the spectra of the elements, or as calculated from the series relationship, along with the multiplet with which the line is classified. This appears to us the most satisfactory way of identifying the lines.

At the same expedition successful plates were taken with spectrographic cameras by Aston and Waley Cohen for the lengths of the chromospheric arcs.

At the same eclipse Curtis and Burns[†] extended knowledge of the spectrum in the infra-red; they obtained the oxygen triplet 7,772 A., 7,774 A., and 7,775 A. (unresolved) and the Ca^+ pair at 8,542 A. and 8,662 A.

In 1930 Mitchell[‡] published a description of his spectra obtained in 1905 and 1925, using a large concave grating giving a dispersion of 10·8 A. per mm. The length of spectrum covered was from 3,318 A. to 6,191 A. in 1905 and from 3,300 A. to 7,065 A. in 1925.

The excellence of the focussing and the large dispersion makes this the most complete spectrum of the chromosphere. By the addition of Stratton and Davidson's results from 3,066 A. to 3,300 A. no less than 3,250 lines are given. Exception may be taken to the identification of every line with a line or group of lines in Rowland's solar spectrum, in view of the difference of dispersion and the dissimilarity of the spectra.

In the view of the authors it is better to compare directly with the spectra of the elements in their normal and ionized states, gradually working down in intensity till lines are no longer seen. Many faint chromospheric lines will be unidentified, but identification of such lines by other methods is of little value.

For comparison of a line spectrum and spectrum of arcs taken by a prismatic camera, an illustration (Plate 5) is given of the chromospheric spectrum taken by the Greenwich expedition to Parent in Canada at the eclipse of 1932 August 31.

The observations by Campbell in 1898, 1905, and 1908 and published by Campbell and Menzel[||] in 1931 introduced a new feature of great value into the photography of the 'flash' spectrum. Instead

† *Publ. Allegheny Obs.* **6**, 95 (1925).   ‡ *Ap. J.* **71**, 1 (1930).
|| Lick Observatory Publications, vol. xvii.

of discontinuous exposures of arcs of the Sun's limb as shown in
Plate 6, Campbell† inserted a slit 0·05 inch wide placed less than
0·02 inch in front of the photographic plate, thus permitting only
a small portion of the arc to be photographed. The plate was moved
uniformly in the direction of the spectral lines as shown in Fig. 17,
taken from the Lick Observatory volume. An exposure of 24 seconds
was given, the speed of the plate in 1905 being 0·06 inch per second,

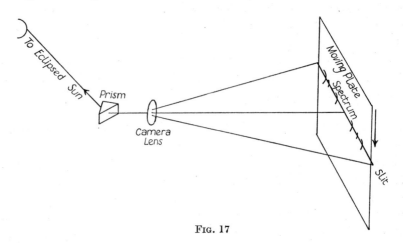

Fig. 17

the effective exposure along any section being about 1 second. The
accompanying illustration gives an unenlarged print extending from
the violet side of Hζ (3,889 A.) to beyond the Mg lines (5,184 A.).
In the Lick Observatory volume five enlargements are given, and
the one extending from 4,130 A. to 4,450 A. is reproduced. These
photographs show to the eye the nature of the reversal of the lines
and give the best description of the Sun's surface for a few thousand
kilometres above and below the chromospheric level. Generally
speaking, the stronger lines are reversed lower down and extend
to greater heights. Attention is drawn by Menzel to the different
behaviour of some lines, for example 4,215 A. Sr⁺ and 4,227 A. Ca.
The latter reverses sharply just inside the disk, while the former is
reversed at a great depth. In addition to the moving plates arc
spectra obtained in 1905 were used to a limited extent. The plates
have been carefully measured and discussed by Menzel. In the
identification of the lines he used solar lines, but bore in mind the
differences between the spectra as regards ionized lines, the multiplet

PLATE 6

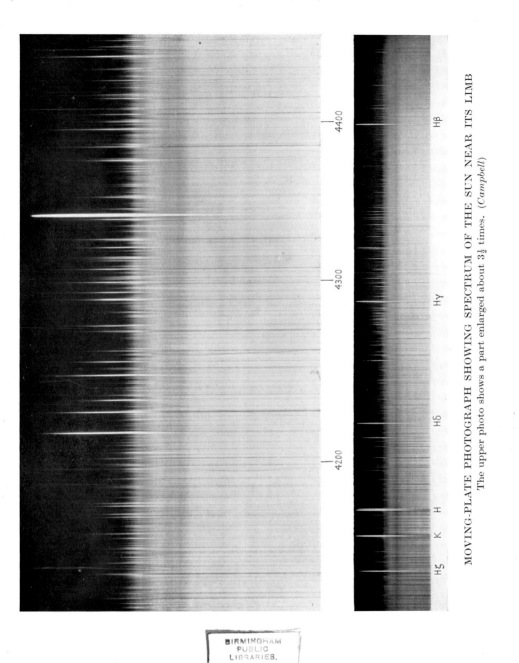

MOVING-PLATE PHOTOGRAPH SHOWING SPECTRUM OF THE SUN NEAR ITS LIMB

The upper photo shows a part enlarged about 3½ times. (*Campbell*)

classification, and the behaviour of the lines in King's furnace spectra. The heights of the lines are given and the depth below the chromosphere at which reversal takes place.

A study of the region from 3,913 A. to 4,466 A. was made by means of a Moll microphotometer, and the intensities determined at the heights 170, 385, 600, 1,030, 1,675, and 2,320 km. are given in a separate table.

In a third table the intensities of the lines of different elements in the flash are given along with excitation potential, spectral classification and the wave-lengths given by laboratory researches.

Menzel follows this up by a study of the chromosphere, dealing with its density gradient, abundance of elements, and the various theories of its equilibrium. He makes a comparison of the 'moving' plate with the 'arc' spectra to determine the heights of lines. He points out clearly that the heights determined by either method cannot be separated from the intensity of the line and the speed of the plate.

Description of the Flash Spectrum. The main features of the spectrum of the chromosphere are as follows. It differs from the Fraunhofer spectrum in that the relative intensities of the lines are greatly changed, the enhanced lines (lines due to ionized elements) being greatly strengthened in the chromosphere. The strongest lines are those due to Ca^+, H, and K. The Balmer series of hydrogen is also strong; nearly forty lines in this series have been identified by several astronomers, and the continuous spectrum at the head of the series may also be seen. Helium and ionized helium are present. Ionized metals including the rare earths are very prominent, and some cyanogen and carbon bands are shown.

The chromospheric spectrum was found by Lockyer and Baxendall to be of earlier type than that of γ Cygni (F8p), and it was found by Dunham[†] that the spectrum of α Persei, a giant star of type F5, bore a remarkable resemblance to that of the chromosphere, both as regards the degree of ionization and the presence of the rare earths.

The heights to which the lines extend may be measured on prismatic camera plates and also on moving camera plates. To some extent the height estimated for any line depends on the length of the exposure, the sensitivity of the plate, etc., but relative heights may

† *Contributions from Princeton Univ. Obs.* **9** (1929).

be obtained from the same plate. The results which have been found
from time to time are as follows:

	Davidson and Stratton	Mitchell	Menzel
	km.	km.	km.
Ca+, H, and K lines . . .	9,200	14,000	10,000
Hydrogen Hα	8,400	12,000	9,000 (Hβ)
Helium D3	7,500	7,500	..
Na and Mg	1,200	1,500	..
Ionized Fe, Ti, Cr . . .	2,500	2,500	..
Neutral Fe, Ti, Cr . . .	..	250–400	..
Carbon and cyanogen bands .	..	300–500	..

The case of helium is peculiar, as the line is not particularly strong
in the lower chromosphere, but extends to great heights. There is
no evidence to show that the heights change from one eclipse to
another.

LINE INTENSITY IN THE CHROMOSPHERIC SPECTRUM

Direct Observations of Intensity in the Spectrum of the Chromosphere. The first observer to measure intensity of emission lines in eclipse spectra was Schwarzschild at the eclipse of 1905, who measured the emissions from four prominences in the Balmer series from $H\beta$ to $H\xi$ and in the Ca^+ lines H and K. Schwarzschild found that the ratio of calcium emission to hydrogen emission is not constant from one prominence to another, but varies by a factor of 10; taking as unit of intensity the intensity in 1 A. at the wave-length concerned in the spectrum of a black body radiating at $6,000°$, the ratio of K to $H\beta$ was 0·31, 1·0, 1·4, and 3·0 in four prominences examined. There is some evidence of a real variation in the Balmer decrement from one prominence to another. Schwarzschild's relative intensities in the units already mentioned give the following mean values:

$H\beta$	$H\gamma$	$H\delta$	$H\xi$
1	0·35	0·10	0·06

Observations of this kind were not repeated until 1926, when Davidson and Stratton measured the Balmer decrement and relative intensities inside certain groups of lines known as multiplets within which the relative intensities are predicted by theory. It is unfortunate that photographic photometry was not introduced into the programme of the 1926 eclipse until a late date, so that no time was available for the construction of adequate calibration apparatus, and the results obtained were only of a provisional character and depend on the assumed value of the Schwarzschild coefficient p in the law connecting I the intensity of the light, D the density of the image on the photographic plate, and t the exposure time, viz. $D = f(It^p)$. In the discussion of the results of this expedition, by Davidson, Minnaert, Ornstein, and Stratton, the intensities are reduced in triplicate with three values of p. Further, as the Sun itself was used to compare intensities in different wave-lengths, it is necessary in reducing the results to assume a colour temperature for the Sun.

The measurements of intensity are discussed in four groups: (1) the intensities of the lines in nine multiplets were measured; (2) the intensities of the lines in the Balmer series from $m = 15$ to $m = 28$

were measured; (3) a number of Ti^+ multiplets were measured at different heights—in the flash at a height of 700 km. above the limb and in a prominence at a height of 14,000 km.; and (4) the continuous spectrum at the head of the Balmer series was examined, both in the flash spectrum and in the spectrum of a prominence.

(1) The relative intensities of the lines in the multiplets agreed pretty well with theoretical expectations. The authors note that Plaskett's colour temperature of the sun (6,400° K.) and a value of $p = 1.0$ for Schwarzschild's coefficient bring about the best agreement.

(2) It was found that the relative intensities of the Balmer lines in a prominence did not agree with theoretical expectations. The theory which is here tested implicitly is twofold; firstly, that the Einstein coefficients of the lines are those given by a certain formula, and secondly that the assembly of hydrogen atoms is partitioned among the various atomic states as if the assembly was in thermodynamical equilibrium 'at the temperature of the prominence'. The investigators were unable to reconcile their observed intensities with any reasonable temperature; this may accordingly be interpreted as showing that the assembly is not partitioned as in thermodynamical equilibrium; but there was never any *a priori* reason for supposing it to be so.

Suppose that there are N_l atoms per c.c. in the state whose total quantum number is l, and let A_{l2} be the Einstein coefficient for spontaneous transitions from state l to state 2. Then the number of transitions from state l to state 2 per c.c. per sec. is $N_l A_{l2}$. Now if the assembly is in thermodynamical equilibrium at a temperature T, N_l is proportional to $\exp(-Rh/l^2kT)$, where R is Rydberg's constant and k is Boltzmann's constant.

According to Schrödinger and Pauli,

$$A_{l2} = \frac{(l-2)^{2l-3}(3l^2-4)(5l^2-4)}{l(l+2)^{2l+3}}.$$

Then for large values of l, $A_{l2} \propto l^{-3}$. The relation which is tested is $I_l \propto l^{-3}\exp(-Rh/l^2kT)$, and this relation is found to be violated. For example, in a comparison between the lines $l = 15$ and $l = 28$ in a prominence at a height 14,000 km., the ratio I_{15}/I_{28} is twice that given by the theory, with $T = 5,000°$. No reasonable value of T will bring about an agreement, the temperatures indicated being absurdly low.

Treated in the same way, Schwarzschild's results yield *far too high* a temperature for the prominence, and they are supported by other evidence; the conclusion to be drawn is that the prominence is not in thermodynamical equilibrium.

(3) Assuming for the moment that the several regions of the upper solar atmosphere are characterized by temperatures, it is possible to compare the temperature of a prominence with that of the flash without a knowledge of the transition coefficients. In thermodynamical equilibrium at a temperature T the number of atoms in a state whose excitation potential is χ is proportional to $\exp(-\chi/kT)$. Comparing the emissions from two places at temperatures T and T', we have

$$I/I' = \exp\left\{-\frac{\chi}{k}\left(\frac{1}{T}-\frac{1}{T'}\right)\right\},$$

where it is supposed that there is no self-reversal of the lines. In the spectrograms obtained at the 1926 eclipse there were ten Ti+ multiplets available in the flash at a height of 700 km. and in a prominence at 14,000 km. On plotting $\log_e I - \log_e I'$ against χ it was found that

$$\left(\frac{1}{T'}-\frac{1}{T}\right) = \frac{1}{27,400}.$$

If we put $T = 5,000°$ for the flash, we get $T' = 4,200°$ for the prominence, but this very reasonable result should not persuade us that the atoms in the prominence are partitioned as if in thermodynamical equilibrium, in face of the other evidence.

(4) The well-known continuous spectrum at the head of the Balmer series shading off into the lines of that series was observed both in the flash spectrum and in the spectrum of a prominence. To compare the intensity distribution in this continuous spectrum with theory, we might assume (*a*) that the chromosphere or prominence is scattering sunlight according to some law, say a λ^3 law, or (*b*) that the molecules in the chromosphere are emitting radiation corresponding to a temperature characteristic of their molecular velocities, the two mechanisms giving the same result in thermodynamical equilibrium with a λ^3 law. Choosing assumption (*b*), the authors find a velocity temperature of $4,000°$ for the flash spectrum and $3,200°$ for the prominence.

The photometric observations of the ultra-violet continuous spectra of flash prominence and Corona attempted at the 1926 eclipse have not yet been repeated; although efforts have been made to do so, these have been frustrated by cloud, for example at the eclipse of 1932. On account of the rough methods of photometry that were used in 1926, the work stands in need of repetition with careful photometry. When this has been done, however, we should not be surprised to find that the temperatures found for a prominence in different ways do not agree with one another, as it appears likely that there are very wide departures from thermodynamical equilibrium in the prominences. Theory as well as observation stands in need of refinement.

Observations of Intensity in the Flash Spectrum in 1927. The flash spectrum from 4,154 A. to 4,768 A. was photographed on 1927 June 29 by Pannekoek and Minnaert† at Gällivare, Lapland. On this occasion exhaustive preparations were made, and a complete photometric calibration of the photographic plates was carried out. On one plate a good flash spectrum was secured at about the time of second contact. Five later exposures show none of the flash spectrum except the lines Hγ and He 4,472 A. The relative intensities of the lines in the flash spectrum were determined from the first plate, and the remaining plates were used to give the decrease of intensity of Hγ and He 4,472 A. as the Moon moved across the Sun and covered up successive portions of the chromosphere.

The intensities of a number of multiplets in the flash spectrum were measured: these intensities do not agree with theoretical results for a thin layer of gas, and Pannekoek and Minnaert attribute the divergence to self-absorption. The legitimacy of using this mechanism in explanation of anomalous multiplet intensities depends presumably on the height in the chromosphere to which the measures refer. Our criterion derived on p. 86 is that self-absorption is negligible if the flash lines are faint compared with the limb spectrum; in the reproduction of Pannekoek and Minnaert's flash spectrum, the flash lines appear to be about as intense as a continuous spectrum from a Baily bead, so that the flash spectrum may refer to so low a level in the chromosphere that self-absorption is appreciable. This point is of importance: we suppose from the results of 1926 and 1927 that the multiplet intensities are normal at a height of 14,000 km., but are distorted by self-absorption in the true 'flash'.

This point has been investigated by Menzel in his discussion of Campbell's spectrograms, which were taken at the eclipses of 1900,

† *Verhandelingen d. K. Akad. Wet. Amsterdam,* **13** (1928).

1905, and 1908. These spectrograms were not calibrated for micro-photometry, but Menzel has reduced them, using the best possible estimate of the calibration curve for converting photographic density into light intensity. Menzel compares observed intensities with theoretical multiplet intensities and attributes differences to self-reversal; he then finds that self-reversal diminishes with decreasing intensity of the line or with increasing height above the limb, and his estimates of self-reversal agree within reasonable limits with those of Pannekoek.

The Balmer Decrement in the Prominences in 1927. At this eclipse Doorn† made two exposures with a prismatic Corona camera designed to give a great light grasp, so that the relatively faint Corona would show on the photographs with short exposures dictated by the circumstances of an eclipse. The diameter of the solar image in any wave-length given by this camera is less than 3 mm.; the dispersion consists of a liquid prism (containing ethyl cinnamate) working against two glass prisms in such a way that the deviation for green rays is zero and the length of the spectrum from Hα to Hξ is 67 mm. Exposures were made (a) from $+5^s$ to $+8^s$ after the beginning of totality, and (b) from $+11^s$ to $+27^s$. Both spectrograms show faint monochromatic rings at 6,375 A., 5,303 A., and 3,987 A., a well-exposed continuous spectrum of the Corona, and very intense chromospheric rings due to the Balmer series; He lines at 4,472 A. and 4,026 A., Sr^+ lines at 4,216 A. and 4,078 A., and the Ca^+ lines at 3,969 A. and 3,934 A. Photometric calibration of the plates was performed by imprinting a set of intensities on sister plates: a lamp emitting light like a black body at 2,662° was used with a step wedge, the exposure times of the comparison spectra being 9^s, 90^s, and 900^s.

The prominences produced images so black that the calibration exposures of 900^s had to be used for comparison. The discrepancy between the exposure times on prominence and laboratory colour standard was unfortunate, as there appeared to be a substantial difference between the relative sensitivities of the red-sensitive plate (an Ilford panchromatic plate) on which Hα was recorded and the Lumière Opta plate, adjacent to the panchromatic plate, which received the image of the spectrum from 4,900 A. to the ultra-violet for short and long exposures. This appears in Pannekoek and Doorn's discussion of the work as a difference between the Schwarzschild

† Ibid. **14,** 21 (1930).

coefficient for the two plates. There is also a certain amount of extrapolation of the calibration data necessary to compare the very black prominence images with the calibration spectra. Nevertheless, relative intensities of the lines in the Balmer series from Hα to Hξ (excepting Hε which coincides with Ca⁺) were determined by Pannekoek and Doorn. These may be compared with the Schrödinger-Pauli formula, assuming the prominences to be in thermodynamical equilibrium (Pannekoek and Doorn call attention explicitly to the illegitimacy of this assumption). Apparent temperatures of 9,100° and 11,000° are found for two prominences, the determinations depending chiefly on the intensity of Hα relative to the other lines. The authors consider that their photometry is so far from being rigid that a temperature of 6,000° is not excluded, but the higher temperatures are in agreement with other observations.

Observations of the Balmer Decrement without Eclipse. The prominences are, of course, quite readily observed without an eclipse, and the Balmer decrement has been measured from Hβ to Hη at Poulkovo by Perepelkin,† using a photographic method, and from Hα to Hβ at Greenwich by Woolley and Newton‡ visually. Perepelkin's results are in good agreement with those of Schwarzschild, and indicate, in the mean, an apparent temperature of 8,000°, while the Greenwich visual result indicates a temperature of about 20,000°. A theory of the Balmer decrement in prominences has been put forward by Woolley,‖ who finds that the apparent temperature Hα to Hβ should be of the order 16,600°, but that the temperature indicated by the lines near the head of the series should be the radiation temperature of the Sun, or about 6,000°. The atoms are distributed among the stationary states in a manner which deviates markedly from thermodynamical equilibrium, and the temperature of the prominence (however defined) cannot be inferred in a simple manner from the Balmer decrement.

The Relative Abundance of the Elements and their Distribution with Height in the Chromosphere. The relative abundance and distribution of the elements in the lower chromosphere has been determined independently by Menzel†† and Mitchell and Miss Williams,‡‡ who used the method developed by H. N. Russell in his

---

† *Poulkova Obs. Circular*, **13** (1935).   ‡ *M.N.R.A.S.* **96**, 5 (1935).
‖ *M.N.R.A.S.* **96**, 515 (1936).   †† *Lick Obs. Publ.* **17**, Part 1 (1931).
‡‡ *Publ. Leander McCormick Obs.* **5**, 197 (1933).

determination of the relative abundance of the elements in the reversing layer. In general, the strength of a spectral line either in emission or absorption depends on the product of the number of atoms in the state responsible for the formation of the line and an atomic coefficient, one form of the latter being the oscillator strength of the line, usually denoted by the symbol f. Suppose that the spectral line is produced by an atom in the state s having an excitation potential χ_s: then if there are N atoms of the element in question per c.c. of the atmosphere, there will be NA_s per c.c. in the state of the atom which produces the line; if the atmosphere is in thermodynamical equilibrium at a temperature T, $A_s = q_s/q_0 \exp(-\chi_s/kT)$, where q_s, q_0 are the statistical weights of the state s and the ground state of the atom, and k is Boltzmann's constant. The absorption coefficient of the line is equal to that of the number $N_{sf} = NA_{sf}$ of classical oscillators (i.e. electrons in the classical electromagnetic theory executing simple harmonic motions with the frequency of the spectral line). The values of f are known in a few cases, but are usually unknown except that relative values of f are known within certain groups of lines known as multiplets.

Now suppose that there is any physical characteristic P which has a one to one correspondence with the intensity of the line: this characteristic may be a direct measurement of the intensity, or the width of the line, or a number on Rowland's scale of intensities, or in the case of atoms known to be distributed similarly in the chromosphere, it might be the length of the arc in the flash spectrum. There will be a relation

$$P = F(N_{sf})$$

between the characteristic P and the 'number of atoms forming the line', or strictly speaking the number of classical oscillators equivalent to the atomic transitions forming the line. The function F should ideally be given from theoretical considerations alone, but the current theory can only be applied to photometric material taken from standardized photographic plates, while some characteristic P may be taken from an unstandardized plate for which it is necessary to derive an empirical relation $P = F(N_{sf})$. This empirical relation is built up from the observed relation between P and N_{sf} in as large a number of multiplets as are available: as only the relative numbers N_{sf} are known, only relative numbers of atoms enter into the calibration, and the number of atoms in the atmosphere might be doubled

M

(leaving the proportion among different elements and states unaltered) without affecting the function F. When the calibration has
been effected by means of the multiplets, the reverse relation
$N_{sf} = F^{-1}(P)$ is used to determine relative numbers of atoms N_s
from observed values of P, in those cases where f is known. The
correlation between the intensity assigned by Rowland in his estimate of line intensity in the normal solar spectrum and the relative
number of atoms forming the line was determined by Adams, Russell,
and Miss Moore, and applied to the determination of relative abundance in the reversing layer by Russell.

Both Menzel, on the one hand, and Mitchell and Miss Williams,
on the other, applied Russell's method to their own independent
estimates of intensity in the flash spectrum. In Mitchell's case,
ninety-nine multiplets involving about five hundred lines were available for calibrating the intensity scale (determining the function F).
This is four-tenths of the number available to Adams, Russell, and
Miss Moore in calibrating the Rowland scale, but Mitchell believes
that his scale is somewhat more accurate and homogeneous than
Rowland's scale, and residuals indicate that the probable error in
deriving $\log Nf$ from a single line is about 0.3. The two calibrations
establish the important result that the relative abundance of elements
in the lower chromosphere is roughly the same as that in the reversing
layer, which is significant when one comes to consider the mechanism
of the support of the chromosphere.

The results of these two independent investigations are not in
detailed agreement with one another, the probable difference in their
estimates of the logarithm of the number of atoms per c.c. in the
chromosphere minus the logarithm of the number in the reversing
layer for any element being 0.5. They agree, however, that H and the
rare earths are at least ten times as abundant in the chromosphere
as in the reversing layer, and that the chromosphere is rich in Sc,
Ti, and Cr, and deficient in Fe and Co. They also agree in finding
that the chromosphere is markedly deficient in Ca—a fact which is
of great importance in dealing with theories of the chromosphere.
However, Mitchell and Miss Williams, discussing their own results
and those of Menzel, comment on the slender material on which
some of the estimates are based, and conclude that 'within the
limits of error no differences are detectable between the relative
abundances in the [lower] chromosphere and those in the reversing

layer, except that hydrogen is probably more abundant in the chromosphere'.

The Density Gradient of the Chromosphere. At the eclipse of 1927 Pannekoek and Minnaert† made a determination of the law according to which the intensity of Hγ falls off with increasing height above the limb. Six plates were taken near the moment of second contact, the mean moment of exposure lying from 3ˢ before the adopted time of contact to 8·5ˢ after this adopted time. In each

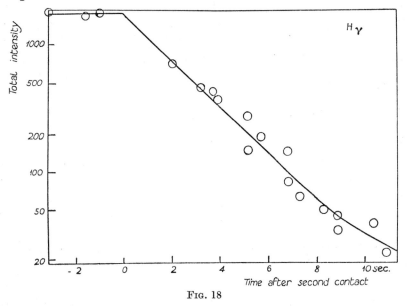

Fɪɢ. 18

plate the intensity of Hγ varies along a line tangential to the Sun's limb on account of irregularities in the Moon's limb: Pannekoek and Minnaert chose three points for investigation, corresponding to a peak and two valleys on the Moon's limb. The curves of intensity of Hγ plotted against time at these three points differ by a phase displacement of the time arising from the fact that the mountain on the Moon covers up a certain layer of the chromosphere before the valley does. Phase differences were estimated so as to reduce the observations to a single curve showing the intensity of Hγ varying with the time after contact (Fig. 18). The total intensity of the chromosphere remains constant until the moment of contact, after which it decreases according to the exponential law $e^{-0.47t}$, where t

† *Verhandelingen d. K. Akad. Wet. Amsterdam,* **13** (1928).

is the time in seconds after contact. Differentiating this expression gives the rate at which the intensity of the chromosphere is falling off: and reducing this expression to heights in kilometres, Pannekoek and Minnaert find that the emission from an arc of the chromosphere of length 1′ of arc and of breadth dH km. at a height H km. above the limb into unit solid angle is

$$2 \cdot 7 \times 10^{20} \exp\left(-\frac{H}{617}\right) dH \text{ ergs/sec.}$$

The line 4,471 He gives altogether different results, showing that He is not uniformly distributed in the chromosphere but is stronger in upper levels, in agreement with earlier observations that the helium lines are relatively stronger in the higher than in the lower chromosphere,[†] and that the arcs of helium are long but intrinsically weak.[‡]

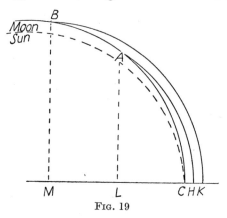

Fig. 19

The distribution of the elements with height in the chromosphere was derived by Mitchell and Miss Williams in an ingenious manner from the lengths of arcs of lines in an objective prism photograph of the flash spectrum. Fig. 19 represents the second or third contact of the eclipse. The Sun's disk is, of course, smaller than the Moon's, and the flash spectrum is the spectrum of solar material extending beyond the Moon's limb. The length of the arc in the flash spectrum in any wave-length depends on the height to which the material reaches; for example, if the material extends uniformly to a height CH above the Sun's limb, the arc of the flash spectrum will be CA, etc., but in fact the material does not extend to a definite boundary but fades away (exponentially) with increasing height, so that on any given photograph the lengths of the arcs will depend on the exposure. The termination of the arc marks a point where the intensity is just sufficient to leave an impression on the photographic plate, and in any range of wave-length

† Dyson, *Phil. Trans.*, Series A, **206**, 449 (1906).
‡ Davidson and Stratton, *Mem. R.A.S.* **64**, 138 (1927).

sufficiently small to ensure that the characteristics of the plate have not changed, the intensity emergent from the chromosphere is the same at the tips of all the arcs.

Mitchell and Miss Williams measured the chords AA', BB' of the flash lines. From these they computed the heights CH, CK, etc., which we may denote by h. In this way they obtain the height h above the limb at which each spectral line emergent from the chromosphere registers a certain threshold intensity I. Bearing in mind the three-dimensional character of the phenomenon, one states

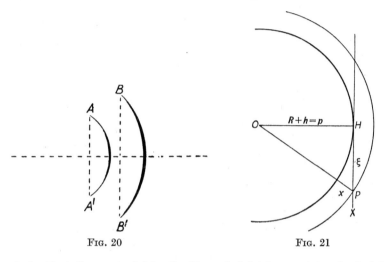

FIG. 20   FIG. 21

precisely that the material in the line of sight tangent to the height CH registers this intensity. Consider the plane containing the line of sight to the point H and the radius from the Sun's centre to that point. Fig. 21 represents this plane; O is the Sun's centre and HX the line of sight. We wish to find out how much light will fall on an object-glass normal to PX which subtends a solid angle $\delta\omega$ to the Sun, and we consider an elementary cylinder along PX. At each point along the cylinder is an element of volume which receives light from all directions (but mostly from the photosphere) and scatters some of it into the elementary solid angle $\delta\omega$ along PX. The flow of energy through 1 sq cm. averaged in all directions at any point P is J, of which the fraction $\alpha J\,\delta v$ is absorbed by the element of volume δv and re-emitted in all directions: the emission into $\delta\omega$ along PX is $\alpha J\,\delta v\delta\omega/4\pi$. Let $I\,\delta\omega/4\pi$ be the flow of energy into the elementary solid angle $\delta\omega$ along PX at any point P. The element of volume δv

at P removes from the flow I the amount $\alpha I\,\delta v\delta\omega/4\pi$ and contributes the amount $\alpha J\,\delta v\delta\omega/4\pi$. The differential equation governing the flow I is therefore
$$dI = \alpha(J-I)\,d\xi,$$
where $d\xi$ is the element of length along PX, and $HP = \xi$.

Let $OH = R+h = p$, and $OP = p+x$. Then $\xi^2 = (p+x)^2-p^2$, and since the extent of the chromosphere is small compared with the radius of the Sun, we may take x/p to be small compared with unity and set $x = \xi^2/2p$. Further, the absorption coefficient α contains the number of atoms per c.c. of the atmosphere at the height x above some datum. Let us suppose that $n = n_0(Ae^{-2p\lambda^2x}+Be^{-2p\mu^2x})$, where $A+B = 1$. Then $\alpha = \alpha_0(Ae^{-\lambda^2\xi^2}+Be^{-\mu^2\xi^2})$ and
$$dI = \alpha_0(Ae^{-\lambda^2\xi^2}+Be^{-\mu^2\xi^2})(J-I)\,d\xi,$$
$$\frac{dI}{J-I} = \alpha_0\,(Ae^{-\lambda^2\xi^2}+Be^{-\mu^2\xi^2})\,d\xi.$$

We now suppose that J is constant, and integrate from $\xi = -\infty$ to $\xi = +\infty$, remembering that $I = 0$ where $\xi = -\infty$. Then if $I = I_1$ where $\xi = +\infty$, we have
$$\log\frac{J}{J-I_1} = \alpha_0\sqrt{\pi}\left(\frac{A}{\lambda}+\frac{B}{\mu}\right),$$
and if I_1/J is small, $I_1 = \alpha_0 J\times$ constant $= n_0 J\times$ constant and the intensity seen along PX is proportional to n_0, the number of atoms per c.c. at H. If I_1/J is small, that is, if the emergent intensity is faint compared with the intensity of the disk, there is no appreciable reabsorption and we may compare theory with experiment exactly as if the eclipse photographs referred to a radial section through the chromosphere. This condition is certainly fulfilled by the tips of the flash lines.†

To return to the work of Mitchell and Miss Williams, let $n(h)$ be the number of atoms of a certain kind at a height h above the limb. The intensity at the tips of the arcs implies a definite number of oscillators $n(h)f$ in each case, where the height h is derived from the observed extent of the arc. Consider a multiplet in which the relative values of f are known, say $f_1, f_2,..., f_n$, and the corresponding

---

† The position is slightly complicated by the different exposure times for different heights in Mitchell's work, and by the failure of the spectrograph to resolve different layers in the moving-plate spectrogram, but the criterion of the effect of self-reversal is unaltered.

heights are h_1, h_2,..., h_n. Then

$$n(h_1)f_1 = n(h_2)f_2 = \ldots = n(h_n)f_n.$$

The function $n(h)$ will be the same for all members of the multiplet. The multiplet gives us n points on the graph of $n(h)$ against h, and the information may be grouped together for all multiplets referring to (say) Fe atoms in a state of excitation less than one volt.

Menzel determined the distribution of density with height in the chromosphere from the lengths of the lines on moving-plate spectrograms of the flash. The method employed is almost identical in the underlying theory but is quite different in detail. We will describe the method here, for the purpose of exposition, as if it were a variant of Mitchell's method; in fact, of course, Menzel's work appeared first. In place of Mitchell's arcs Menzel measures the heights to which lines extend in his moving-plate spectrum. The tips of the lines A, B are heights above the Sun's limb at which the intensity is just sufficient to leave an impression on the photographic plate under the conditions of exposure, and therefore give directly the heights h at which each spectral line registers a certain threshold intensity I —exactly as in the other method. As before, the intensity at the tip of each arc implies a definite number of oscillators $n(h)f$. The graph of $n(h)$ against h could be obtained from the multiplets as was done by Mitchell, but Menzel preferred to make use of his scale of intensities which had already been calibrated on the multiplets for the work on abundance. All the material is thrown together without attempting to distinguish between different types of lines (i.e. between atoms in different states of ionization and excitation). Menzel also reduced his results by an alternative method, making use of line intensities measured with a microphotometer, which gave $n(h)f$ directly: although the original plates had not been calibrated for photometry the results are in good agreement with those derived from the multiplet intensities. Both reductions are in good agreement with the results of Mitchell and Miss Williams.

The results are as follows:

Number of atoms at a height H in kilometres

Menzel, all atoms:

From multiplet intensities . . . . $\exp\left(-\dfrac{H}{4050}\right) + 59\exp\left(-\dfrac{H}{1560}\right)$

From microphotometer intensities . . . $\exp\left(-\dfrac{H}{3580}\right) + 56\exp\left(-\dfrac{H}{1650}\right)$

Mitchell and Williams:

Ti II . . . . $\exp\left(-\dfrac{H}{5000}\right)+60\exp\left(-\dfrac{H}{2000}\right)$

Fe I of E.P. 1 volt . . . . . $\exp\left(-\dfrac{H}{3333}\right)+50\exp\left(-\dfrac{H}{1667}\right)$

Pannekoek and Minnaert:

H . . . . $\exp\left(-\dfrac{H}{617}\right)$

The result found by Pannekoek and Minnaert is added for completeness.

THE EQUILIBRIUM OF THE CHROMOSPHERE

The Theory of Selective Radiation Pressure. It can easily be shown that the chromosphere is not in hydrostatic equilibrium under solar gravity alone. Consider an atmosphere consisting of singly ionized atoms of atomic mass M and electrons under no forces except solar gravity: let P be the total pressure, ρ the density, g the acceleration due to solar gravity, and x the height above some surface. The condition of hydrostatic equilibrium is

$$dP = -g\rho \, dx. \tag{1}$$

In an isothermal atmosphere consisting of ions of mass M and electrons of negligible mass, we have

$$P = \rho \,.\, 2kT/M. \tag{2}$$

Integrating equation (1) we get

$$\rho = \rho_0 \exp\!\left(-\frac{Mgx}{2kT}\right), \tag{3}$$

where ρ_0 is the density at the height $x = 0$. Taking the case of an average atomic weight such as that of calcium, we set $M = 40$, and if we set $T = 6,000°$ and reckon x in kilometres, we get

$$\rho = \rho_0 \exp(-0\!\cdot\!11x),$$

so that the density decreases by a factor e^{11}, or about 10^5 in 100 km., which is altogether at variance with the results found by Menzel and by Mitchell and Miss Williams. It is clear, then, that the chromosphere receives support in some way. The first suggestion as to the nature of this support was put forward by Milne,† who suggested radiation pressure as a supporting agent. In particular, ionized calcium is subject to selective radiation pressure on account of the fact that its principal lines occur at 3,934 A. and 3,968 A., which is not too far removed from the wave-length of maximum solar radiation, and it can be shown at once that in this case the upward support due to selective radiation pressure is comparable with solar gravity. Although selective radiation pressure cannot be invoked as the cause of support of the chromosphere generally, since it is much smaller for all other elements, and although it is observed that Ca^+ does not extend higher into the chromosphere than other elements, the theory

† *M.N.R.A.S.* **85**, 111 (1924).

of the support of the calcium chromosphere by selective radiation pressure is one of great interest.

To simplify the problem, let us suppose that there is only one line in the spectrum of Ca$^+$ (the lines H and K considered as a single line). Let the energy density of the outward flux in the centre of the Fraunhofer line be F. The atom will absorb from the flux F an amount of energy $f(\pi e^2/m)F$ ergs per sec., and the upward momentum absorbed by the atom per second is $f(\pi e^2/mc)F$. The factor f is the oscillator strength of the line, e and m are the charge and mass of the electron, and c is the velocity of light.

Now the flux F is the energy density of outward flowing solar radiation at the wave-length of the line multiplied by a certain ratio r, called the central intensity of the line, which is the ratio of the flux in the centre of the Fraunhofer line to the flux at wave-lengths just outside the line. Let us suppose that the Sun is radiating like a black body at some temperature T. The energy density of the outward flux is then one-half of the energy density of full radiation as given by Planck's law, and we have

$$F = \tfrac{1}{2}rB_\nu, \qquad B_\nu = \frac{8\pi h\nu^3}{c^3}\frac{1}{e^{h\nu/kT}-1}. \tag{4}$$

Here h is Planck's constant and ν is the frequency of the centre of the Fraunhofer line. It is convenient to have a symbol, μ, for the ratio of the upward force due to selective radiation pressure to the downward force due to solar gravity. Then

$$\mu = \frac{1}{Mg}\tfrac{1}{2}rB_\nu f\frac{\pi e^2}{mc}. \tag{5}$$

The principal lines of Ca$^+$ are in fact two, at 3,968 A. ($f = \tfrac{1}{3}$) and 3,934 A. ($f = \tfrac{2}{3}$). If we suppose that the central intensities of these two lines in the chromospheric absorption spectrum are equal, we can treat them as one line at 3,951 A. for which $f = 1$. If we assume $T = 6,000°$, we find from (5) that $\mu = 1$ if $r = 0.02$.

It is a difficult matter accurately to measure the central intensities of the narrow chromospheric lines H_3 and K_3, but the central intensities are probably less than 0.10, and the observational evidence suggests that μ is of order 1, i.e. that there is an approximate balance between radiation pressure and gravity on a Ca$^+$ atom. Let us suppose at first that $\mu < 1$. We shall have in place of (3) a new equation

$$\rho = \rho_0\exp\left\{-\frac{(1-\mu)Mgx}{2kT}\right\}, \tag{6}$$

whence it follows that selective radiation pressure forces the selected element to stand out to a greater height than that attained by an atmosphere in which there is no selective radiation pressure. This is most easily seen in the case where there is a solid boundary at $x = 0$, such as a planetary surface, but there is of course no such simple lower boundary to the solar atmosphere. But we can make use of the physical conditions which prevail in the reversing layer to form a lower boundary for the chromosphere. In the reversing layer all elements are present in abundance and the support given by selective radiation pressure is small compared with gravity. Neutral Ca and electrons are present which will control Π, the partial pressure of Ca$^+$. We idealize the reversing layer in our mathematical description of the solar atmosphere by describing the reversing layer as a surface at which the Ca$^+$ partial pressure Π takes some determined value Π_0, and we choose this surface as our origin of coordinates $x = 0$. Then from (6)

$$\Pi = \Pi_0 \exp\left\{-\frac{(1-\mu)Mgx}{2kT}\right\}. \tag{7}$$

We have to make a similar simplification of the radiation problem. If there are N atoms of a particular kind above some surface $\xi = 0$, the central intensity of the principal absorption lines r occurring in equations (4) and (5) will be given by some equation of type

$$r = F(Ns_\nu), \tag{8}$$

where s_ν is the atomic scattering coefficient for the frequency ν corresponding to the (centre of the) absorption line. To illustrate this explicitly we refer to Schuster's model of the atmosphere in which a definite number of absorbing atoms are placed in front of a radiating surface. (In the actual solar atmosphere radiating layers and absorbing layers are not distinct in this simple way.) Let ξ be the height above the radiating surface, or photosphere, N the number of Ca$^+$ atoms in a column of unit cross-section above the surface $\xi = 0$. Then

$$r = \frac{1}{1+Ns_\nu}. \tag{8 a}$$

Let N_0 be the number of Ca$^+$ atoms per sq. cm. of the reversing layer, i.e. the number of Ca$^+$ atoms in a column of unit cross-section between the surfaces $\xi = 0$ and $x = 0$. Then

$$N = N_0 + \int \frac{\Pi}{kT}\, dx = N_0 + \frac{2\Pi_0}{(1-\mu)Mg}. \tag{9}$$

In addition, we have (5) or

$$\mu = f\frac{\pi e^2}{mc}\frac{1}{2}\frac{rB_\nu}{Mg},\tag{10}$$

so that the quantities μ, r, and N can be determined if we suppose Π_0 and N_0 known: notice that the value of r is predicted from theory. It should, of course, be possible to predict on a purely theoretical basis just how much a chromosphere should stand out from an ordinary atmosphere: but there are difficulties. There are some obvious weaknesses in this idealized treatment, and the adoption of surfaces for boundary conditions may be called into question. Similar methods have not met with complete success when applied to the central intensities of the Fraunhofer lines, and it may be supposed that the phenomenon of fluorescence, which appears to have an important bearing on central intensities, should not be ignored, as we have done in our adoption of equation (8). But while a more elaborate theory would modify the boundary conditions, while a more exact theory of the formation of lines would transform equation (8 a), our simplified treatment illustrates in principle the support of a chromosphere by radiation pressure. At the present time it is useless to pursue the matter further by inserting numerical values and solving the equations, because it is impossible to assign a value to N_0, and because we are without a satisfactory formula for the connexion between r and N to replace equation (8).

The bearing of the observational evidence (Chapter XI) on the theory of the support of the chromosphere is discussed very fully by Mitchell and Miss Williams.† If the density distribution of the chromosphere is proportional to $\exp\{-(1-\mu)Mgx/2kT\}$, then on account of the increase of ionization with height the distribution of neutral atoms is approximately proportional to

$$\exp\left\{-\frac{(1-\mu)Mgx}{2kT}\right\}+\tfrac{3}{2}C\exp\left\{-\frac{(1-\mu)Mgx}{kT}\right\},\tag{11}$$

the value of C depending on the electron pressure at $x = 0$. This equation does not fit Mitchell and Miss Williams's observed data perfectly. In the chromosphere at a height between 1,500 km. and 2,400 km. above the limb lines from both Fe and Ti+ give results which are fairly close to Pannekoek and Minnaert's observed gradient for Hγ, namely, $N \propto \exp(-H/617)$, where H is the height in km.

† *Ap. J.* **77**, 209 (1933).

Applying Mitchell and Miss Williams's figure for Fe, $N \propto \exp(-H/500)$ or $N \propto \exp(-2x \times 10^{-8})$, we get either

$$\frac{(1-\mu)Mg}{2kT} = 2 \quad \text{or} \quad \frac{(1-\mu)Mg}{kT} = 2,$$

according to which term of the equation (11) is supposed predominant. We must have either $(1-\mu) = 0 \cdot 01$ or $(1-\mu) = 0 \cdot 005$, and in either case the support given by selective radiation pressure to Fe is absurdly high. Again, the ultimate lines of Fe^{+} lie in a region of the spectrum where the intensity of the spectrum is only one-third of that which contains the ultimate lines of Ti^{+}, yet the observed density gradients are the same within the limits of error; finally, the density gradient of H above 1,000 km. is only slightly smaller than that of other elements, whereas the value of B_{ν} appropriate to the principal lines of hydrogen (the Lyman series) is about one-millionth part of the value appropriate to the H and K lines of Ca^{+}.

The Special Case of Complete Support. Before leaving the theory of hydrostatic equilibrium with support by selective radiation pressure, we go on to outline some work of great interest by Milne. In the special case $\mu = 1$ the radiation pressure exactly balances gravitation and the solution (7) is not applicable. To obtain a solution we have to go more fully into the physics of the problem, and the condition itself, adjusted to fit a more refined theory, becomes the condition that $\mu = 1$ at the upper boundary. When the Ca^{+} atom absorbs a quantum of resonance radiation, the valence electron moves from the ground state S to the state P, in which it cannot absorb another quantum of the resonance radiation. Atoms whose electrons are raised into the P state are transparent to the resonance radiation, and get no support from it. Now the number of atoms whose electrons are in the P state is proportional to the density of the radiation field, which increases as we go below the surface (although the net outward flux remains constant). Accordingly, if $\mu = 1$ at the upper surface, $\mu < 1$ below the surface, and the atoms are supported by the gradient of a small gas pressure, which dies away to zero at the upper surface.

Let $J(\theta)$ be the flow of radiation per sq. cm. per sec. in a direction making an angle θ with the outward normal to the Sun's surface. Let J_1 be the average value of $J(\theta)$ for outward directions, $0 \leqslant \theta \leqslant \frac{1}{2}\pi$,

J_2 the average for inward directions, $\frac{1}{2}\pi < \theta \leqslant \pi$, and let $d\omega$ be the element of solid angle. F is as before the net outward flux. Then

$$J_1 = \int_0^{\frac{1}{2}\pi} J(\theta)\frac{d\omega}{4\pi}, \qquad J_2 = \int_{\frac{1}{2}\pi}^{\pi} J(\theta)\frac{d\omega}{4\pi}, \qquad F = \int_0^{\pi} J(\theta)\cos\theta\frac{d\omega}{4\pi}.$$

We now introduce the conception of optical depth (due to Milne) If there are n atoms of Ca$^+$ in the ground state per c.c. of the atmosphere at a height x, then the optical depth τ is defined by

$$\tau = -\int^{\infty} ns_\nu\, dx.$$

The (approximate) equations governing the transfer of radiation through the atmosphere are†

$$\left.\begin{aligned}
F &= \text{const.}\\
J_1 &= 4F(1+\tfrac{3}{4}\tau)\\
J_2 &= 3F\tau\\
J &= \tfrac{1}{2}(J_1+J_2) = 2F(1+\tfrac{3}{2}\tau)
\end{aligned}\right\} . \qquad (12)$$

Let n_1, n_2 be the numbers of Ca$^+$ atoms per c.c. in the ground state S and the excited state P respectively, and let a_{12}, a_{21}, and b_{21} be the Einstein transition coefficients.‡ Then the number of upward transitions per second is equal to the number of spontaneous downward transitions plus the number of stimulated downward transitions per second, or

$$n_1 a_{12} J = n_2 b_{21} + n_2 a_{21} J.$$

Hence
$$\frac{n_2}{n_1} = \frac{a_{12} J}{b_{21}+a_{21} J} \doteqdot \frac{a_{12}}{b_{21}} J. \qquad (13)$$

The spontaneous emission $n_2 b_{21}$ is sent out equally in all directions and gives no momentum to the atom, but the stimulated emission $n_2 a_{21} J$ is in the direction of the stimulating radiation, and has accordingly an outward flux $n_2 a_{21} F$ contributing a downward momentum to the atom. This reduces the net outward momentum on an atom in the ground state, and the ratio μ is reduced from μ_0 (given by (10)) to

$$\mu_0 \times \frac{n_1 a_{12} F - n_2 a_{21} F}{n_1 a_{12} F}.$$

The effective value of μ for an assembly of atoms is still further reduced in the ratio $n_1/(n_1+n_2)$ by the fact that radiation pressure

† Eddington, *Internal Constitution of the Stars*, pp. 322, 365.
‡ As defined by Eddington, ibid., p. 47.

is not exerted on the atoms in the upper state. We have, accordingly, for the effective ratio of radiation force to gravity

$$\mu = \mu_0 \times \frac{n_1 a_{12} - n_2 a_{21}}{n_1 a_{12}} \frac{n_1}{n_1 + n_2}.$$

Now $\dfrac{a_{21}}{a_{12}} = \dfrac{q_1}{q_2}$, where q_1, q_2 are the statistical weights of the ground state S and excited state P (equal to 2 and 6 in the case of Ca$^+$). Hence if n_2/n_1 is small,

$$\mu = \mu_0 \left\{ 1 - \left(\frac{q_1}{q_2} + 1 \right) \frac{n_2}{n_1} \right\}.$$

At this stage we want to modify the condition $\mu_0 = 1$ by taking account of spontaneous emission and elevation into the P state, the adopted boundary condition being that $\mu = 1$ at the top of the chromosphere. Let $\mu_0 = (1 + \sigma)$. Then

$$\mu = (1 + \sigma) \left\{ 1 - \left(\frac{q_1}{q_2} + 1 \right) \frac{n_2}{n_1} \right\}, \tag{14}$$

the constant σ being determined by the boundary condition that $\mu = 1$ at $\tau = 0$. At the boundary we have

$$J = \tfrac{1}{2} r \times \frac{8\pi h \nu^3}{c^3} \times \frac{1}{e^{h\nu/kT} - 1},$$

and

$$\frac{n_2}{n_1} = \tfrac{1}{2} r \times \frac{q_2}{q_1} \frac{1}{e^{h\nu/kT} - 1};$$

we find that $\mu = 1$ gives

$$\sigma = \left(\frac{q_1}{q_2} + 1 \right) \frac{n_2}{n_1} = \frac{2r}{e^{h\nu/kT} - 1}. \tag{15}$$

Now n_2/n_1 is proportional to J (by (13)) and therefore to $(1 + \tfrac{3}{2}\tau)$; inserting the value $q_1/q_2 = \tfrac{1}{3}$ in (14) and neglecting small terms, we get, after some reduction,

$$\mu = 1 - \tfrac{3}{2}\tau\sigma.$$

Then
$$d\Pi = -g\rho \, dx (1 - \mu) = \tfrac{3}{2} g\rho\tau\sigma \, dx,$$

and since $d\tau = -\rho s_\nu \, dx$,
$$\frac{d\Pi}{d\tau} = \frac{3}{2} \frac{g\tau\sigma}{s_\nu}.$$

Integrating,
$$\Pi = \frac{3}{4} \frac{\sigma g}{s_\nu} \tau^2,$$

since $\Pi = 0$ at $\tau = 0$. In an isothermal atmosphere $\Pi = \rho kT/M$, so that

$$\rho = \frac{3}{4}\frac{Mg\sigma}{kTs_\nu}\tau^2.$$

Now
$$d\tau = -\rho s_\nu \, dx = -\frac{3}{4}\frac{Mg\sigma}{kT}\tau^2 \, dx.$$

Hence
$$\tau = \frac{4}{3}\frac{kT}{Mg\sigma}\frac{1}{(x+x_0)}, \tag{16}$$

x_0 being a constant of integration. We arrive finally at a relation between ρ and x, which is what we are looking for. It is†

$$\rho = \frac{4}{3}\frac{kT}{Mg\sigma s_\nu}\frac{1}{(x+x_0)^2}. \tag{17}$$

This gives the distribution of density ρ with height x above an arbitrary level of the chromosphere.

Eddington‡ arrives at the value of x_0 in the following way. We have by (12) $J_1 = 4F(1+\frac{3}{4}\tau)$. Now let H be the efflux of solar radiation at wave-lengths just outside the Fraunhofer line: then outside the line $J_1 = 4H$. Eddington points out that the energy intensity inside the line cannot have values greater than the neighbouring continuous spectrum, or

$$F(1+\tfrac{3}{4}\tau) \not> H$$

for all τ. Now $F = rH$, so that the intensity of radiation inside the line becomes equal to that of the neighbouring spectrum at an optical depth τ_0 such that

$$r(1+\tfrac{3}{4}\tau_0) = 1,$$

or
$$\tau_0 = \frac{4}{3}\frac{1-r}{r}.$$

Accordingly τ_0 is an upper limit to the optical thickness of the chromosphere. If we take the depth τ_0 as the optical depth of the base of the chromosphere and measure x from this base, i.e. put $x = 0$ at $\tau = \tau_0$, we have from (16)

$$x_0 = \frac{kT}{Mg\sigma}\frac{r}{1-r}.$$

But r is given by (15). We have accordingly

$$x_0 = \frac{1}{1-r}\frac{kT}{2Mg}(e^{h\nu/kT}-1). \tag{18}$$

---

† Milne, *M.N.R.A.S.* **65**, 125, 1924.   ‡ Op. cit. **336**.

Neglecting r in $(1-r)$, taking $M = 20$, solar gravity $2\cdot74 \times 10^4$ cm./sec.^{2} and $T = 6,000°$, we get $x_0 = 1,900$ km. The density of the chromosphere is accordingly proportional to

$$(x+1,900)^{-2},$$

where x is the height in kilometres. Thus at a height 1,900 km. the density has fallen to one-quarter of its value at the base, etc. It must be remarked that it is impossible to reconcile this density distribution with the observed density distribution.

Chandrasekhar's Theory of the Dynamics of the Chromosphere. A variant of Milne's theory of selective radiation pressure as the mechanism of support of the chromosphere is due to Chandrasekhar.† This writer takes as fundamental the observed fact that the solar surface appears granulated. The flux of radiation is accordingly non-uniform, and in Chandrasekhar's view a hydrodynamical and not a hydrostatic equilibrium is to be looked for. The mathematical theory, restricted for simplicity to two dimensions, proceeds as follows. It is assumed that $\mu = 1 + r\sin(2\pi x/\lambda)$, where x is a coordinate along the Sun's surface and λ is a wave-length fundamental to the atmosphere. Notice that the average value of μ is unity, so that gravitation is on the average exactly balanced by selective radiation pressure. Having made this assumption, it is possible to calculate the trajectory of an atom projected with a given velocity at any point in the atmosphere. The boundary of the chromosphere is the envelope of the atomic trajectories.

Writing $2\pi x/\lambda = \xi$, $2\pi z/\lambda = \zeta$ (where z is measured along the vertical), Chandrasekhar finds the following equation for the trajectory of a particle:

$$\sin\xi = \frac{\alpha}{\beta} \int_{\zeta}^{\zeta_0} \zeta K_1(\zeta)\, d\zeta,$$

where α, β are constants and ζ_0 is the point at which the trajectory intersects the ζ-axis. The function $K_\nu(\zeta)$ is given by

$$K_\nu(\zeta) = \frac{\Gamma(\nu+\frac{1}{2})(2\zeta)^\nu}{\Gamma(\frac{1}{2})} \int_0^\infty \frac{\cos\xi\, d\xi}{(\xi^2+\zeta^2)^{\nu+\frac{1}{2}}},$$

the functions being related to Hankel functions with imaginary arguments, thus

$$K_\nu(\zeta) = \tfrac{1}{2}\pi i e^{\frac{1}{2}\nu\pi i} H_\nu^{(1)}(i\zeta).$$

† *M.N.R.A.S.* **94**, 13 (1933).

According to the circumstances of projection, the trajectories are periodic in ξ, in which case the particle is identified with the normal chromosphere, or aperiodic, in which case the particles are considered by Chandrasekhar as being emitted, as in eruptions. The law of density distribution in Chandrasekhar's chromosphere is

$$\rho = \rho_0 \frac{2}{\pi} \int_\zeta^\infty \zeta K_1(\zeta)\, d\zeta,$$

which approximates closely for values of ζ greater than 1 to the law

$$\rho = \rho_0 \exp(-0\cdot 87\zeta).$$

The mean horizontal velocity of the atoms is given by

$$\bar{\bar{\xi}} = 3\cdot 9 \times \sqrt{\left(rg\frac{\lambda}{2\pi}\right)}.$$

There are accordingly two disposable constants in the theory, λ and r, though these must be chosen to fit the appearance of calcium spectroheliograms. Chandrasekhar adopts $\lambda = 20,000$ km. and $r = \frac{1}{3}$. He finds that the limiting vertical velocity of an atom expelled in an eruption is

$$\zeta_\infty = \sqrt{\left(rg\frac{\lambda}{2}\right)} = 30\cdot 2 \text{ km./sec.}$$

This is in good agreement with an observation of H. W. Newton, who found that the most frequent inward and outward velocity of dark $\mathrm{H}\alpha$ flocculi associated with sun-spots is between 20 and 40 km./sec.: further, with this value of λ the density distribution agrees tolerably well with the observations of Mitchell and Miss Williams.

Despite these successes, Chandrasekhar's theory is only of theoretical interest because it does no more than Milne's original theory in the way of accounting for the support of the chromosphere: that is to say, if the physical conditions are such that $\mu = 1$ approximately, Milne's hydrostatic equilibrium is possible and so is Chandrasekhar's hydrodynamical equilibrium. We have already said that the condition $\mu = 1$ can only be true for Ca^+, yet the other elements behave in the same way as Ca^+. There is also a certain difficulty in selecting a definite wave-length λ. Recently H. H. Plaskett[†] measured the ratio of the intensity of solar granules to the intergranular space, finding a maximum value of $1\cdot 10$, which means that r is not greater than $0\cdot 05$. To preserve the velocity $\zeta_\infty = 30$ km./sec. we must have $\lambda = 130,000$ km. giving $\rho = \rho_0 \exp(-H/33,600)$ which does not agree

† *M.N.R.A.S.* **96**, 432 (1936).

with observed density gradients (pp. 87–8), which are roughly $\exp(-H/1,700)$ for the lower chromosphere and $\exp(-H/4,000)$ for the upper chromosphere.   There is also a difficulty connected with the mean horizontal velocity of which Chandrasekhar himself is aware: even with $\lambda = 20,000$ km., $\bar{\xi} = 66$ km./sec., as compared with 18 km./sec. inferred by Unsöld from line-contour observations.

Transfer of Momentum from Ca^+ to other Elements; Viscosity. We have noticed the experimental results quoted by Mitchell and Miss Williams which show that the chromosphere appears to be well mixed, so that if selective radiation pressure exercised on certain elements supports the chromosphere there must be some means whereby the momentum is transferred from one kind of atom to another, e.g. from Ca^+ to H. The only mechanism which suggests itself is viscosity. Of course, viscosity can play no part in a static atmosphere, but if we accept the fact (which is of course obvious from a number of types of solar observation) that the gases in the Sun's atmosphere are in motion, then they may drag each other about through viscosity. The only calculations appear to be those of McCrea,[†] who finds that the viscosity is of such an order of magnitude that the solar gases should drag each other about. We can accordingly imagine a quasi-equilibrium of the chromosphere in which Ca^+ is upthrust by a local excess of radiation pressure and drags other elements upwards with it. These other elements would be prevented from falling rapidly elsewhere by their viscous drag on Ca^+ which would receive upward support from radiation pressure. Again by appealing to viscosity we can modify Chandrasekhar's theory, which applies strictly speaking to an atmosphere consisting of Ca^+ alone, to a general atmosphere. This modification has never been made in detail. It may, however, easily be demonstrated that the total upward momentum available from selective radiation pressure is insufficient to support the mixture of atoms actually found in the chromosphere against solar gravity—in other words, $\mu \ll 1$ for the atmosphere as a whole.[‡] It seems right, therefore, to say that while selective radiation pressure may be responsible for particular outbursts of solar gases, it cannot be responsible for the support of the chromosphere, and we turn to alternative theories of chromospheric support.

† *M.N.R.A.S.* **95**, 509 (1935).
‡ This fact was pointed out to the authors by Prof. McCrea in a letter.

Turbulence. The theory of turbulence as applied to the chromosphere is due to McCrea.† This theory was developed in order to account for the presence of hydrogen, and other elements to which selective radiation pressure gives no support, in the chromosphere. It is obvious from spectroheliograms and from spectrohelioscope observations that there is a great deal of motion on the solar surface. It is easy to see, from a physical point of view, that the dynamical pressure of a gas is as much influenced by the independent motions of atoms with pure temperature velocities as by motions of the atoms in groups or clusters, the dimensions of the groups being small compared with the dimensions of the whole chromosphere. McCrea supposes that the gas can be divided into volume elements of finite extent Δ such that the atomic motion in each group is temperature motion (the temperature corresponding to the ionization and excitation exhibited by the chromosphere), but the elements Δ themselves have a Maxwellian distribution in velocity corresponding to a temperature $\mathbf{T}$ characterized by a mean velocity C. Some complications arise when the material is not homogeneous, but in the case of an atmosphere consisting of nothing but neutral hydrogen

$$k\mathbf{T} = kT + \tfrac{1}{3}MC^2,$$

where M is the mass of the hydrogen atom. The pressure p is given by

$$p = nk\mathbf{T},$$

where n is the number of hydrogen atoms per c.c.

McCrea quotes data obtained by Unsöld.‡ This observer measured the contours of the H and K lines of Ca^+ in emission in the chromosphere and the corresponding absorption lines H_3 and K_3, and deduced that the contours can only be explained by a Doppler effect corresponding to a mean velocity C of 18·4 km./sec. This is about ten times the temperature velocity, and Unsöld attributes it to turbulence. McCrea accordingly puts $C = 18\cdot4$ km./sec. This gives $\mathbf{T} = 18,630°$. Now if H represents a height in kilometres, we have, with $T = 6,000°$,

$$\exp\left(-\frac{MgH}{kT}\right) = \exp\left(-\frac{H}{1,807}\right),$$

$$\exp\left(-\frac{MgH}{k\mathbf{T}}\right) = \exp\left(-\frac{H}{561}\right),$$

---

† *M.N.R.A.S.* **89**, 718 (1929).   ‡ *Ap. J.* **69**, 207 (1929).

so that the supposition that $\mathbf{T} = 18,000°$ agrees closely with Panne-koek and Minnaert's observations of the density gradient of Hγ and with Mitchell and Miss Williams's values for Fe and Ti$^+$ at a height of 2,000 km.

Chandrasekhar has criticized McCrea's theory on the ground that the turbulence parameter $\mathbf{T} = 18,630°$ is introduced *ad hoc* to account for the observed density distribution in the chromosphere, but in fact McCrea took it as a datum of observation from Unsöld's measurements. But even if $\mathbf{T} = 18,630°$ had no basis whatever except the observed density distribution of the chromosphere, the adoption of this parameter is no more unwholesome than the acceptance of the parameter $\mu = 1$ for all elements. Finally, in defence of the turbulence theory, it is necessary to rebuff the suggestion that there is a difficulty connected with the Maxwellian distribution of the velocities of the elements Δ. According to Milne (quoted by Chandrasekhar), the Maxwellian distribution implies exchange of momenta between the groups, but the groups cannot exchange momenta without the individual atoms taking part in the collision process. But McCrea's theory does not demand any exchange of momentum between the groups to create the Maxwellian distribution of velocities: if the name is changed to a Gaussian distribution, its appearance as the result of haphazard forces below the solar surface becomes intelligible. McCrea is aware of the fact that turbulence must be maintained against dissipative forces: it is suggested that the energy comes from the break-up of laminar flow below the solar surface.

Support by Momentum derived from Coronal Streamers. Yet another manner in which the chromosphere may be supported has been described by Rosseland.† Norwegian physicists have constantly under their notice the phenomenon of the aurora borealis, and it is supposed that it is excited by electric particles issuing from the Sun. It is known, for example, that the frequency and magnitude of auroral displays goes with the sun-spot cycle. Further, the plumed and tufted nature of the Corona suggests that the coronal streamers are composed of electrons ejected from the Sun, their paths being bent by the solar magnetic field. Rosseland supposed that there is a continuous ejection of high-speed negatively charged electrical particles. Their expulsion will leave the sun positively charged and this will produce an outward drift of positive ions moving under

† *Publ. Univ. Obs. Oslo,* **5**, (1933).

the repulsive electric force. This drift carries the chromospheric atoms to the observed heights. This theory of the mechanism of the support of the chromosphere merits the careful attention of investigators.

We may sum up this discussion by saying that the mechanics of the support of the chromosphere are not yet fully understood. It is useless to attempt at the present moment to decide between one theory and another of the nature of its support: but while admitting that a further five years' research may well cause the scientific world to revise its views on this question, the authors incline to the view that turbulence represents the most satisfactory solution of the problem of the support of the chromosphere. It must be said that Chandrasekhar's theory represents the correct solution of the particular assumptions on which it is based. The question is, whether $\mu = 1$ and any value of λ really correspond to conditions on the Sun. The fundamental distinction between Chandrasekhar's theory and McCrea's is this value of μ, and there is a degree of similarity between a set of gas-pressure forces distributed in a Gaussian manner and a set of radiation-pressure forces distributed as granulations over the surface. An examination of spectroheliograms suggests that a random distribution of radiation-pressure forces is preferable to a sine distribution.

XIII

PHOTOGRAPHY OF THE CORONA. THE SOLAR CYCLE

PHOTOGRAPHY of the Corona is usually included in the programme of expeditions for observation of total eclipses. These are not mere mementoes of the occasion, but have a definite scientific value, showing the extent of the streamers and their relationship to the prominences, and also the form of the Corona at different states of the solar cycle. Photographs on a large scale giving a diameter of the Moon's disk of 4, 5, or 6 inches with short exposures show how the inner Corona is related to the prominences which happen to be on the Sun's limb on the day of the eclipse. Longer exposures near mid-totality show the forms of the streamers to distances of about 30' from the limb and give the features of the Corona in detail. To obtain the extent of the Corona, smaller lenses of short focal ratio are employed which may show streamers extending over several degrees.

Owing to the great falling off in the intensity of the Corona from the limb, it is impossible to obtain all the details on a single photograph. Drawings have frequently been made to combine the results of photographs taken with different exposures. These necessarily sacrifice the relative intensity of the coronal light near and far from the limb, but give a useful representation of the whole Corona with the prominences on the Sun's limb. The careful drawings by W. H. Wesley[†] of the Coronas at the eclipses of 1871, 1882, 1886, 1898, 1900, 1901, 1905, 1908 may be cited as examples. The paintings of the eclipses seen in the United States in 1918, 1923, and 1925 by Mr. Howard Russell Butler[‡], which hang in the American Museum of Natural History, not only give the beauty of the scene, but are a faithful representation of the forms and colour of the Corona and prominences.

Coronal Arches. Among the features which are better shown in the drawings than in photographic reproductions of the original negatives are the arches seen over prominences, first drawn attention to by Schaeberle in the eclipse of 1893. They are beautifully shown in the Lick Observatory photograph of the eclipse of 1918. It is hardly necessary to make an exhaustive list of these arches, and

[†] *Mem. R.A.S.* **41**; *Phil. Trans.*, Series A, **180**, 119; **226**, 363.
[‡] *Natural History*, July, August 1926, Am. Mus. of Nat. Hist., New York.

we need only refer to Wesley's drawings in *Phil. Trans.* **226,** the drawings of the Corona of 1925 by Slocum,† and of the Corona of 1926 from the Swarthmore College Expedition by Miss Williams,‡ and by Horn D'Arturo‖ at the same eclipse. A series of three or four arches over a prominence is not infrequent, the outer one rising to 5' or 6' above the Sun's limb.

At the eclipse of 1923 Miller and Marriott†† found a disturbed region near the place where spots had been photographed on the previous day. Arches were found here, and by comparison with photographs taken at another station 24 minutes previously they were found to be moving outwards with a velocity of 7 km./sec. With a greater interval of 150 minutes between his own photographs and those taken by Stratton and Davidson, Horn D'Arturo finds velocities of 1·7 km./sec. in height of the arches and 0·7 km./sec. in their width.

These arches and their movements naturally suggest that the condensations and rarefactions in the Corona result from some explosive action causing the prominences.

Changes in Corona. Occasionally a sun-spot occurs near a limb at the time of an eclipse. Here again a disturbance is found in the Corona. Perrine drew attention to one in the eclipse of 1901. A real change appears to have taken place in the hour-and-a-half interval between the eclipse at Mauritius and that at Sumatra. Comparison of Maunder's photograph with Dyson's in Wesley's drawings shows a prominence in the former not seen in the latter, but replaced by a patch which is undoubtedly coronal, slightly to the north of the prominence.

These are evidences of continuous change and movement in the inner Corona in the neighbourhood of both prominences and spots. The longer streamers are frequently to be found in connexion with prominences. Instances may be found in Wesley's drawing of the 1898 Corona, in Slocum's drawing of the 1925 Corona, and in Miss Williams's drawing of the Corona of 1926.

On the other hand, long streamers are frequently found when there is no prominence shown on the limb. Hansky, who examined the prominences on a few days prior and subsequent to the date of the eclipse in 1886, concluded that every coronal ray had a prominence connected with it, though these were not on the limb on the day of

---

† *Ap. J.* **64,** 145 (1926).
‖ *Publ. of Obs. of Bologna,* vol. **1,** no. 8, p. 211.
‡ *A.S.P.* **40,** 91, plate 8.
†† *Ap. J.* **61,** 73 (1925).

PLATE 7

CORONA, 1900. MINIMUM PHASE

CORONA, 1898. INTERMEDIATE PHASE

PLATE 8

CORONA, 1927. MAXIMUM PHASE

CORONA, 1927. MAXIMUM PHASE

the eclipse. Although we are unaware of any extensive verification of Hansky's view, it seems probable that streamers frequently surround prominences, and thus the form of the Corona will change in the course of a few weeks or months.

It was pointed out by Ranyard in 1881 that at sun-spot minimum there was an extension of the Corona in the equatorial direction. In 1887 Hansky[†] collected and published a series of drawings of the Corona arranged according to their phase in the solar cycle.

Later eclipses have amply confirmed Hansky's classification of the forms of the Corona into three types, Equatorial, Polar, and Intermediate.

(1) *Equatorial*. The streamers are entirely in the equatorial direction. Short plumes are seen over an arc of nearly 60° at the north and south poles. E. W. Barnard's photograph of the eclipse of 1900 May 28 is a representative of this class.

(2) *Polar*. The streamers extend in all directions, and the polar plumes are absent. The photograph of the eclipse of 1927 June 29 by the Hamburg Observatory is representative of this type. It is supplemented by Jackson's photograph at the same eclipse showing the inner Corona and prominences.

(3) *Intermediate*. The eclipse of 1898 January 22 is typical of this class. The streamers are not confined to the Equator but do not reach the poles. Polar plumes are not so prominent and are sometimes only seen at one pole.

W. J. Lockyer[‡] in three papers has classified the forms of the Corona from 1857 to 1932 in these three groups. With these he has given in graphical form data of the Sun's mean spotted area, the frequency of prominences, and the mean north and south latitudes of spots and prominences. He defends the view that the forms of the Corona follow more closely the rise of prominences in latitude than the frequency of sun-spots.

Ludendorff[||] has given a quantitative measure of what may be called the ellipticity of the Corona. On photographs of each eclipse he drew 'Isophotes', or lines of equal intensity. He then divided the Corona by lines through the centre of the Moon into 8 equal sectors,

---

† *Bulletin de l'Académie Impériale des Sciences de St. Pétersbourg*, March 8, 1887. See also *Obs. Mag.* **18.**

‡ *M.N.R.A.S.* **63**, 481; **82**, 323; **91**, 797.

|| *Sitz. der Preuss. Akad. d. Wiss.*, 1928, p. 185, and 1934, p. 200.

I in the direction of the Sun's equator, V that of the pole, and so on. He then measured the diameters of each sector of an Isophote and determined the eccentricity as $\dfrac{\text{VIII}+\text{I}+\text{II}}{\text{IV}+\text{V}+\text{VI}} - 1$. Then taking

$$R = \tfrac{1}{3}(\text{VIII}+\text{I}+\text{II}),$$

he formed for each Isophote the equation

$$\epsilon = a_0 + b_0(R-1).$$

He gives as an example the Corona of 1932, where he uses material supplied by Cambron (a member of the Canadian Jesuit Expedition), the Naval Observatory of Washington, and Harvard College Observatory.

R	ϵ	Δ	
1·13	+0·06	−0·02	N
1·18	+0·08	−0·01	N
1·34	+0·12	+0·01	C
1·34	+0·13	+0·02	H
1·48	+0·15	+0·02	H
1·60	+0·12	−0·03	H
1·71	+0·15	−0·03	H
1·71	+0·17	+0·01	H

He finds
$$a_0 = +0\cdot061 \pm 0\cdot017,$$
$$b_0 = +0\cdot143 \pm 0\cdot034.$$

Introducing a small correction to use the radius of the Sun instead of the Moon, he finds

Eclipse	a	b	$a+b$	ϕ
1893	+0·03	−0·03	0·00	+0·82
96	+0·02	+0·22	+0·24	−0·67
98	+0·06	+0·12	+0·18	−0·47
1900	+0·02	+0·28	+0·30	−0·17
01	+0·02	+0·23	+0·25	−0·04
05	+0·01	0·00	+0·01	+0·85
08	+0·06	+0·02	+0·08	−0·78
14	+0·04	+0·15	+0·19	+0·25
18	+0·13	+0·10	+0·23	−0·87
22	+0·03	+0·23	+0·26	−0·15
23	+0·05	+0·17	+0·22	+0·02
25	+0·04	+0·09	+0·13	+0·31
26	+0·05	+0·02	+0·07	+0·50
27	+0·05	−0·01	+0·04	+0·81
29	+0·09	+0·03	+0·12	−0·83
30	+0·04	+0·23	+0·27	−0·57
32	+0·06	+0·14	+0·20	−0·24

$a+b$ corresponds to the ellipticity at a distance of one diameter from the Sun's centre, while ϕ is the phase of the solar cycle which he defines as $(T-m)/(m-M_1)$ or $(T-m)/(M_2-m)$, where M_1 and M_2 are the times of successive maxima of sun-spots and m of minimum. Negative values precede and positive ones follow the minimum. The minima and maxima are taken to be as follows:

Min.	Max.
1889·6	1894·1
1901·7	1906·4
1913·6	1917·6
1923·6	1928·4
1934·0	

Rejecting the Corona for 1918 which is of maximum type on the west and minimum on the east side of the Sun, the accordance of $a+b$ with ϕ is satisfactory after minimum but not good from maximum to minimum. He agrees with Mitchell that equatorial and polar types of Corona occur a year or two before the minima and maxima of the sun-spot period.

Ludendorff compares the ellipticities with the annual means of sun-spots, and the means for the periods of the solar rotation at the time of the eclipse and several previous rotations, but finds no accordance. When, however, he compares the mean area of prominences for the calendar month previous to the eclipse, the results are much more satisfactory. Although he is by no means dogmatic, he agrees with Mitchell† 'that the Corona takes its shape from the lengths and position angles of the longest streamers. It can have no constant shape but no doubt it varies from day to day, depending on the location of the Sun's activity'.

Bergstrand‡ attempts to eliminate the perspective effect of streamers from the Sun in moderately high latitudes on the Isophotes near the pole and so obtain the real instead of the apparent form of the Corona. Using the formula which he derived from the 1914 eclipse, the intensity at height h is $1/h^2$ at the equator and p/h^2 at the pole.

Taking an Isophote whose distance from the limb is h at the equator and h' at the pole, he adds a term $k/(h'+0·5)^2$ for the intensity of the additional light from the streamers in the polar direction. He then has the equation

$$\frac{1}{h^2} = \frac{p}{h'^2} + \frac{k}{(h'+0·5)^2}$$

† *Ap. J.* **75**, 31–2 (1932).
‡ *Archiv für Math. Ast. och Fysik*, Stockholm, **22**A, No. 1; **25**A, No. 4; and *M.N.R.A.S.* **95**, 436 (1935).

which he solves for p and k from the successive Isophotes. The values of p from different eclipses have a value about 0·3 from a year after sun-spot maximum to sun-spot minimum when they gradually increase to 0·7 about a year before the next maximum. Bergstrand suggests that at this point there is a discontinuity in the real form of the Corona which suddenly returns to minimum type. Bergstrand's views are criticized by Ludendorff, who points out the irregularities of the values of k. The empirical form of the term $k/(h'+0·5)^2$ is only justified if the values of k agree in similar cases. The Coronas of 1900 and 1901 are of very similar minimum type, but the values of k are 0·48 and 0·00.

The authors are in agreement with Mitchell and Ludendorff, that the Corona may show different streamers in the course of a few weeks, but the general form which is indicated by its ellipticity is in conformity with the rise and fall in latitude of spots and prominences in the solar cycle.

Photography of the Corona without an Eclipse. In 1882 Huggins attempted to photograph the Corona in full daylight, and the problem received further attention from Hale and Deslandres. Screens, spectroheliographs, and other devices have been tried in vain. Success was attained by Lyot[†] at the Observatory of the Pic du Midi. In a clear sky and with a high Sun the atmospheric diffusion gives to the sky near the Sun a brilliancy of about one-millionth of the Sun for the wave-length 5,500 A., which is not sufficient by itself to overpower the Corona within a few minutes of the Sun's limb. Dust in the air is a more fatal obstacle and according to Lyot's observations at Meudon often surpasses 50 millionths of sunlight and is seldom less than 20 millionths. On the Pic du Midi, especially after a fall of snow, the diffused light is not more than twice the intensity of the Corona. Of still greater importance is the diffusion introduced by the optical system which may amount to one-thousandth part of sunlight and completely mask the Corona. Lyot analyses this diffusion into (1) the effect of diffraction at the edge of the lens, (2) scratches on the surface, (3) small bubbles in the lens, and lastly to a reflection from the two faces of the lens. Plate 9 shows clearly the effect of this diffused light.

Lyot eliminated these defects by constructing a Coronagraph in the following manner. He employed a plano-convex lens of 13 cm.

[†] *Zs. f. Astrophys.* **5**, 73 (1932).

PLATE 9

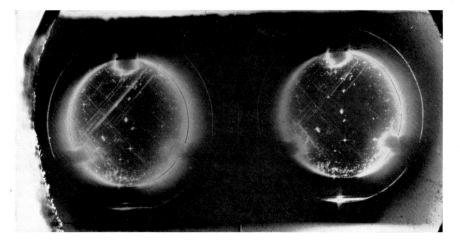

STEREOSCOPIC PHOTOGRAPH SHOWING THE DIFFUSED
LIGHT OF A SIMPLE LENS. (*Lyot*)

CORONA OF 1936 JULY 7. (*Lyot*)

diameter and focal length 3·15 m., figured and polished with the greatest care without scratch or bubble. This lens is placed at *A* and forms an image of the Sun on a blackened brass disk at *B* with a margin of 15″ greater than the disk. A field lens *C* behind the disk produces an image *A'A"* of the lens *A* on the diaphragm *D*, with an additional very small screen *E* at its centre. The diaphragm *D* eliminates the light diffracted from the edge of *C*, and *E* that produced by the light reflected from the two surfaces of the lens. Behind the diaphragm and the screen a strongly corrected objective forms an achromatic image of the Corona at *B'B"*. The field lens, diaphragm, and objective are fixed on a slide *M* to admit of focusing.

The whole apparatus is in a wooden tube *G*, 5 metres long, coated

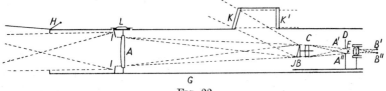

FIG. 22

internally with oil, and closed by a cap at *H* only opened during observation. A silvered concave diaphragm at *I* throws away unwanted light, and a silvered disk at *J* reflects the light through windows at *K* and *K'*, and thus prevents heating of the tube.

With this instrument at an altitude of 2,870 m., at the Observatory of the Pic du Midi, the Corona could on occasions be photographed. Panchromatic plates with a screen admitting light of 6,600 A.– 6,800 A. were used. But these precautions did not wholly succeed in cutting out diffused light. But by mounting the Coronagraph in a carrier which admitted of rotation, comparison of photographs showed what light was truly coronal and what arose from instrumental causes. By the superposition of six photographs taken at intervals of 60° the photograph of the Corona on 1931 July 21 was obtained. It represents the inner Corona corresponding to a diameter of the Moon 1·06 times that of the Sun. Lyot also measured the polarization of the Corona around the Sun's limb, and interpreted the results as an indication of the form of the Corona. By the elimination of all stray light, and by the use of a Lyot diffraction polarimeter,† which

† *Annales de l'Observatoire de Meudon*, 1929.

can detect polarization to 1 part in 1,000, he found no atmospheric polarization within 7′ of the Sun's limb. Polarization commenced at a distance of 6′ from the Sun's limb. It increased rapidly towards the Sun and was stationary at a distance of 3′ to the limb. It was strongest when the sky was most transparent and disappeared at the

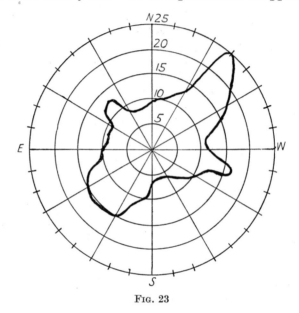

Fig. 23

passage of lightest clouds. The polarization in parts per thousand in different directions at a distance of 80″ from the limb is given in the accompanying diagram, which refers to 1931 July 31 at midday with the Sun's altitude 50°. The form corresponds to the brilliancy of the Corona and not to the proportion of the light polarized, and suggests a resemblance to the form of the Corona, as the poles of the Sun are approximately in position angle 10° and 190°. Reference should be made to Lyot's paper in the *Zeitschrift für Astrophysik*, **5**, 73 (1932), and to the following short notes: *Comptes Rendus*, **191**, 834 (1930); **193**, 1169 (1931); **195**, 943 (1932); **198**, 246 (1934); **200**, 219 (1935); **202**, 391, 1259 (1936).

INTENSITY OF CORONAL LIGHT. TOTAL LIGHT

THE intensity of the coronal light at different distances has been combined by many observers with a determination of its total light. It is convenient to divide such investigations into two parts, and present the determinations of the total light in a later part of this chapter.

Harkness,[†] from visual observations of the eclipse of 1878, gave the law C/h^2, where h is the distance from the Sun's limb.

Turner[‡] found that the visual observations of Abney and Thorpe at the eclipses of 1886 and 1893 could not be satisfied by this law and gave the law $c/(h+0\cdot25)^2$. From photographs taken by himself[||] and Captain Hills at the eclipse of 1898 he was led to the law

$$\text{Brightness} = Ar^{-6}+B,$$

where r is the distance from the centre of the Sun, and B represents the effect of sky illumination. A varies with the radius along which the intensity is measured.

Schwarzschild[††] in the course of an investigation to determine the total light of the Corona, made photometric observations on direct photographs on the outer Corona and spectrophotometric observations on the inner Corona. From the first series he obtained the results:

r	30′	35′	40′	45′	50′
Intensity $J \times 10^8$.	1·60	0·79	0·42	0·23	0·12
Intensity in mags. .	19·5m	20·3m	20·9m	21·6m	22·3m
Turner's law . .	19·4m	20·4m	21·3m	22·1m	22·7m

and from the second series:

r	16·5	18·1	19·6	21·2	22·8	24·4	26·0
Intensity $J \times 10^8$	111·0	42·0	17·0	11·2	6·4	3·7	2·1
Intensity in mags.	14·9m	15·9m	16·9m	17·3m	18·0m	18·6m	19·2m
Turner's law .	15·5m	16·1m	16·6m	17·1m	17·6m	18·0m	18·5m

The intensity J is given in terms of the Sun's mean intensity and in the second line the intensity of the Corona is given in stellar magnitudes. Turner's law A/r^6 becomes in stellar magnitudes $15 \log r$.

[†] *Washington Observations*, **23** (1880).
[||] *Proc. R.S.* **68**, 36 (1901).
[‡] *Proc. R.S.* **66**, 403 (1900).
[††] *Ast. Mitt. Göttingen*, **13**.

Becker[†] at the same eclipse found the law $A(h+0.140)^{-4}$, or in increasing stellar magnitudes $10 \log(h+0.140)$, which he observed at Forsse in Sweden with the Sun at an altitude of 38°.

At the eclipse of 1914 August 21, for which he had made careful preparations, Bergstrand[‡] used objectives by Zeiss achromatized from 3,660 A. to 4,860 A. of 6 inches aperture and 60 inches focal length. Photographs were taken with apertures ranging from 2 to 11 cm., and exposures of 5[s], 10[s], and 20[s]. Scales of blackness were impressed on all photographs before development. The photographs were measured in a Hartmann photometer against scales which had been carefully calibrated by Lundmark.

The following extract from a more complete table gives the different distances from the limb at which the intensity reaches definite stellar magnitudes in the directions of the Sun's pole and other radii.

P	-3.6^m	-2.8^m	-1.7^m	-0.9^m	-0.1^m	$+0.9^m$	$+1.7^m$	$+2.8^m$
0°	0·10	0·17	0·31	0·43	0·65	1·19	1·93	2·77
45°	0·15	0·22	0·37	0·51	0·75	1·30	2·04	3·08
90°	0·18	0·29	0·49	0·66	0·93	1·43	2·17	3·38
135°	0·15	0·31	0·50	0·66	0·84	1·27	2·05	3·13
180°	0·07	0·14	0·26	0·41	0·65	1·21	1·91	3·11
225°	0·21	0·30	0·49	0·63	0·84	1·29	2·08	2·99
270°	0·18	0·28	0·47	0·65	0·99	1·50	2·39	3·45
315°	0·16	0·24	0·34	0·42	0·67	1·21	1·90	2·86

The zero is arbitrarily assumed as 1.00^m at a distance of one radius from the limb on the Equator.

Bergstrand drew Isophotes from these figures. His conclusion was that the law C/h^2 was well satisfied at the Equator. At the poles the law is more nearly $C/h^{1.9}$. He is, however, inclined to a more complicated law to separate the true polar intensity from the projective effect of streamers in latitudes of 30° or greater.

Young,[||] using Perrine's observations for polarization at the eclipses of 1905 and 1908, gave the law A/r^8.

At the eclipse of 1925 January 24 Pettit and Nicholson[††] determined the relative intensity at different parts of the Corona photographically. Exposures of 2[s] and 15[s] were made on Seed 30 plates and of 73[s] on an Ilford panchromatic plate with a red filter, putting standard photometric squares on each plate. The photographs were centred and rotated beneath the slit of a registering microphotometer. The

[†] *Phil. Trans.*, Series A, **207**, 307 (1908).

[‡] *Études sur la distribution de la lumière dans la Couronne Solaire* (Stockholm, 1919).

[||] *L.O.B.* 205.   [††] *Ap. J.* **62**, 202 (1925).

galvanometer readings are converted into intensities on an arbitrary scale by comparison with the photometric squares. The means are taken for each zone and when corrected for general sky illumination and halation the following table obtained.

Mean Intensity for Different Zones

Mean radius	Area A	Intensity I (Seed 30)			$I \times A$	Intensity (Ilford)	$I \times A$
		3^s	15^s	Mean			
1·11	0·355	0·595	0·546	0·570	0·202	0·815	0·289
1·27	0·406	0·228	0·269	0·245	0·100	0·277	0·112
1·43	0·458	0·111	0·137	0·124	0·057	0·126	0·058
1·59	0·509	0·063	0·068	0·066	0·033	0·065	0·033
1·75	0·560	0·039	0·041	0·040	0·022	0·031	0·017
1·91	0·611	0·027	0·027	0·027	0·016	0·016	0·010
2·07	0·662	0·019	0·017	0·018	0·012	0·008	0·005
2·23	0·714	0·015	0·012	0·014	0·010	0·006	0·004
2·39	0·765	0·010	0·009	0·010	0·008	0·004	0·003
2·55	0·816	0·006	0·007	0·007	0·006	0·002	0·002
2·71	0·867	··	0·005	0·005	0·004	0·001	0·001
2·87	0·918	··	0·004	0·004	0·004	0·001	0·001
3·03	0·970	··	0·003	0·003	0·003	0·001	0·001
··	··	··	··	··	0·477	··	0·536

They found agreement with Turner's law of A/r^6 for the Seed plates (4,500 A.), and for the Ilford plates with filter (6,500 A.) the law A/r^7.

E. S. King and Margaret Harwood[†] determined the intensity of the Corona observed at the eclipse of 1925 with a $7\frac{1}{2}$-inch Cooke objective by comparison with the extra-focal images of stars in the Pleiades and in the belt of Orion. By use of an Argand lamp at a distance of 1 metre, squares of known intensity were impressed on portions cut from the plates of the Corona and the stars. Measures were made by a thermo-electric photometer on a large number of points on the Corona. The density was too great for satisfactory measures to be made within 5' of the limb. From 5' to 100' from the limb the intensity is found to vary as h^{-2}.

The eclipse of 1927 was observed by Bolansky and Perepelkin[‡] in Sweden. They were somewhat handicapped by cloud and fog, but secured a number of measurable photographs with a Cooke 4-inch of 4 metres focal length and a Zeiss Tessar of 120 mm. and 60 cm. focal length. With suitable density scales they made measures with a Hartmann microphotometer. They gave special attention to the intensity in the neighbourhood of the arches over the prominences,

[†] H.C.O. Circular 312.   [‡] M.N.R.A.S. 88, 740 (1928).

and note that the isophotes, of which they give a drawing, are drawn in towards the prominences. As a mean result they find

$$m = 5 \cdot 71 + 7 \cdot 5 \log(h + 0 \cdot 146),$$

or that the intensity varies as $(h + 0 \cdot 146)^{-3}$. From observations of the intensity of the continuous spectrum of the Corona by Jenvall[†] from 4,900 A. to 3,910 A. this law was confirmed.

Klüber[‡] made very careful investigations from the large-scale photographs taken by Freundlich in 1929 for the bending of light by the Sun's gravitational field. One of these telescopes had an aperture of 20 cm. and a focal length of 3·4 metres, giving a scale of 1′ to 1 mm., and exposures were made of 30^s, 56^s, and 14^s. The second telescope had an aperture of 20 cm. and a focal length of $8 \cdot 5^m$, so that 1 mm. on the plate was 25″. Three plates with exposures of 90^s, 60^s, and 40^s were measured. Thirty images of graduated darkness with a range of 9 magnitudes were impressed on each plate by use of a lamp of colour temperature corresponding to 3,000°, care being taken to have uniform illumination.

The plates were measured in the Hartmann microphotometer of the Potsdam Astrophysical Observatory. A comparison wedge was, after some experiments, constructed of the same colour and grain as the eclipse photographs. The readings of the wedge were converted into magnitudes by means of the graduated images on each plate. The three photographs of scale 1 mm. = 1′ were first reduced. They were then combined by allowing for the movement of the Moon so as to bring them to the central phase of the eclipse. Klüber drew a series of isophotes from 1^m to 7^m. Assuming the formula $J = C/h^n$ for distances of 6′ to 70′ from the limb, he finds the following values of n for different position angles:

Pos. angle	n	Pos. angle	n
°		°	
0·0	2·6	180·0	2·9
22·5	2·6	202·5	2·4
45·0	2·3	225·0	2·9
67·5	2·5	247·5	2·5
90·0	2·4	270·0	2·4
112·5	2·3	292·5	2·5
135·0	1·9	315·0	2·0
157·5	2·4	337·5	2·0

Near the pole n is 2·0 and near the equator 2·5, and the mean value is 2·4.

[†] *Ast. Jaht. och Under: a Stockholms Obs.* **11**, 8.
[‡] *Zs. f. Astrophys.* **2**, 289; **3**, 142.

He next discussed the photographs taken with the 8·5-metre tele-scope, giving an image of the Sun of 7·3 cm. or nearly 3 inches, from which he obtained the following diagram of the isophotes.

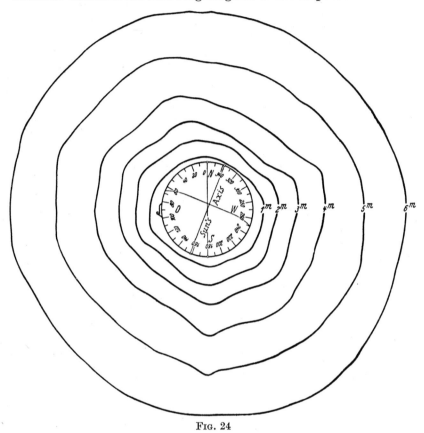

FIG. 24

As before, solving for different position angles for the value of n in the formula A/h^n, he finds:

Pos. angle	n	Pos. angle	n
°		°	
0·0	2·0	180·0	2·3
22·5	2·3	202·5	2·2
45·0	2·0	225·0	2·3
67·5	2·3	247·5	2·0
90·0	2·2	270·0	2·0
112·5	2·1	292·5	2·0
135·0	2·0	315·0	1·9
157·5	1·9	337·5	1·9

The mean result is 2·1, ranging from 1·9 at the poles to 2·3 at the Equator. Although the difference between the two results is small, he gives greater weight to the earlier determination.

The brightness of the Corona at the eclipse of 1926 January 14 was determined by Stetson and Andrews† from photographs taken by Miller with a camera of 6 feet focal length. Standard squares were impressed on the plates before development and the opacity of 300 points from the Moon's limb to a distance of five radii determined. We are in entire agreement with the authors' conclusion that the brightness of the Corona cannot be expressed as a simple function of the radial distance either from the limb or the Sun's centre.

For the region 2·0–2·55 solar radii they find a law varying as r^{-7};

| ,, | ,, | 2·55–3·1 | ,, | ,, | ,, | r^{-4}; |
| ,, | ,, | 3·1–5·0 | ,, | ,, | ,, | r^{-2}; |

and no evidence for any appreciable difference at different eclipses.

The following table is mainly extracted from Klüber's paper.

Year	Observer	Law	Limits	Max. or min.	Sun-spot number at date of eclipse
1878	Harkness	h^{-2}	..	Min. 1878·9	3·4
1893	Turner	$(h+0·2)^{-2}$	0 to 2·6	Max. 1894·1	84·9
1898	Turner	$(h+1)^{-6}$	0·1 to 3·0	Min. 1901·7	26·7
1905	Schwarzschild	$(h+1)^{-6}$	0·1 to 1·3	Max. 1906·4	63·5
1905	Becker	$(h+0·14)^{-4}$	0·1 to 1·7	Max. 1906·4	63·5
1905	Young	$(h+1)^{-8}$	0·07 to 0·6	Max. 1906·4	63·5
1908	Abbot	$(h+0·14)^{-4}$	at a few points	Min. 1913·6	48·5
1908	Young	$(h+1)^{-8}$	0·07 to 0·6	Min. 1913·6	48·5
1914	Bergstrand	h^{-2}	0·1 to 4·0	Min. 1913·6	9·6
1925	Pettit	$(h+1)^{-6}$	0·1 to 2·0	Min. 1923·6	44·3
1925	Nicholson	$(h+1)^{-7}$	0·1 to 2·0	Min. 1923·6	44·3
1925	King and Harwood	h^{-2}	0·7 to 5·7	Min. 1923·6	44·3
1926	Stetson and Andrews	various	2·0 to 6·0	Min. 1923·6	63·9
1927	Balanowski and Perepelkin	$(h+0·15)^{-3}$	0·05 to 3·1	Max. 1928·4	69·0
1927	Jenvall	$(h+0·15)^{-3}$	0·08 to 0·4	Max. 1928·4	69·0
1929	Klüber	$h^{-2·5}$	0·8 to 4·7	Max. 1928·4	65·0
1929	Klüber	$h^{-2·1}$	0·8 to 4·7	Max. 1928·4	65·0

The different laws show no relationship to the type of Corona. On the whole they are not more discordant than one would anticipate from photographs of the Corona. The table of magnitude differences which follows illustrates some of the laws.

† *Ap. J.* **69**, 227 (1929).

Law \ h	0·1	0·2	0·3	0·4	0·5	0·75	1·0	1·5	2·0	3·0	4·0	5·0
h^{-2}	0·0	1·5	2·4	3·0	3·5	4·4	5·0	5·8	6·5	7·4	8·0	..
$h^{-2\cdot5}$	..	..	..	..	3·1	4·2	5·0	6·0	6·9	8·0	8·8	9·4
$(h+0\cdot15)^{-3}$	0·0	1·1	1·9	2·6	3·1	4·2	5·0	6·2	7·0	8·2	..	..
$(h+0\cdot14)^{-4}$	−1·3	−0·3	0·8	1·7	2·5	3·9	5·0	6·5	..	..	..	..
$(h+1)^{-6}$	1·1	1·7	2·2	2·7	3·1	4·1	5·0	6·5	7·6	9·5	..	..
$(h+1)^{-8}$	0·2	0·9	1·6	2·3	2·9	4·2	..	..	..	..	..	..

Total Light of the Corona. The total light of the Corona may be obtained by concentrating it in a suitable manner and comparing it photometrically with a standard candle. This may be done visually, photographically, or by means of a photo-electric cell. Another method is to measure the intensity in different parts and then by mechanical integration or by a determination of the law of intensity obtain the total light.

Some of the earlier observations give very large or very small values of the total light in comparison with that of the full Moon. The large values in all probability included a good deal of scattered daylight in the result. As the apparent diameter of the Moon may be 1·08 times that of the Sun, and the intensity of the light falls off very rapidly from the Sun's limb, variations of 30 to 40 per cent. may be expected in different eclipses. No variation due to the solar cycle has as yet been established. The total light of the Corona is about half that of the full Moon.

Among the earlier visual observations are:

1886   Abney and Thorpe *Phil. Trans.* **180**, 363 0·8 full Moon
1889, Jan. Leuschner   Lick Obs. 1889   0·4 ,,   ,,
1893   Abney and Thorpe *Proc. R.S.* **66**, 403   1·1 ,,   ,,

These were obtained by the use of a Rumford or similar photometer by comparing the intensities with a standard candle at various distances.

Turner determined the brightness from photographs taken by Abney in 1893 and by himself and Hills in 1898. A series of darkened squares were prepared by Abney which transmit light over a range of four magnitudes. By the light of a standard candle at a measured distance, these were printed on the plates with the same time of exposure as was given in the eclipse. Exposures of 1^s, 2^s, 8^s, and 20^s were given at the eclipse of 1898. Corrections of $+0\cdot45^m$, $-0\cdot15^m$, $+0\cdot22^m$, $-0\cdot15^m$ were made to bring the plates into harmony, the larger correction to the plate with 1^s exposure being assumed as due to error of time of exposure. The plates were then measured in a photometer, the law $A/r^6 + B$ deduced, where A/r^6 is the intensity of the Corona at distance r from the centre of the Sun, and B the sky illumination.

For the eclipse of 1898 A was found to be 1·2, taking the Moon as equivalent to 0·02 of the standard candle at the distance of one foot. By integration, the total light of the Corona was found to be 1·1 the full Moon. The eclipse of 1893 treated in a similar manner gave 0·6. The main uncertainty about this determination is the value of the photographic light of the standard candle compared with the full Moon.

At the eclipse of 1905 visual determinations were made by Fabry[†] and Knopf[‡] and photographic determinations by Schwarzschild[||] and Graff.[††]

Fabry used a Lummer photometer to measure the total light of the Corona. A circle of 5° round the eclipsed Sun was thrown on the screen by a telescope with a Huyghens eyepiece. The tint of the comparison light was harmonized by passing its light through an ammoniacal solution of copper sulphate. The standard lamp was then determined in terms of the light of the lamp used during the observation. He finds the light of the Corona = 0·13 lux (i.e. light of standard candle at distance of one metre). Taking the light of the full Moon as 0·175 lux, the total light of the Corona = 0·75 full Moon. For the intrinsic light he found at a distance of 5′ from the limb a value of 0·28 of the full Moon, agreeing satisfactorily with Turner's value of 0·25.

Knopf using a Weber photometer and a benzene lamp as an intermediary comparison found for the total light of the Corona a value 0·85 of the full Moon.

Schwarzschild reduces Fabry's value of 0·75 to 0·55 on account of the diffused light. A similar reduction of Knopf's value brings it down to 0·62 of the full Moon.

Schwarzschild made a photographic determination of the intensity of the Corona, and then by integration the total light. For the outer Corona he used a small telescope with a Petzval objective of 6 inches and a focal length of 28 inches. For the inner Corona he determined

---

† Fabry, *C.R.* **141**, 870 (1905).   ‡ Knopf, *Hamb. Abhand.* **3**, 79 (1913).
|| Schwarzschild, *Ast. Mitt. Göttingen*, **13** (1906).
†† Graff, *Hamb. Abhand.* **3**, 47 (1913).

the intensities from a spectrum extending from 5,000 A. to 3,500 A. obtained with an objective prism of violet glass and 45° angle and an object-glass of 4·4 inches and focal length 44 inches. The intensities were determined by comparing the blackness with photographs of the Sun taken through a darkened wedge at different readings. These were compared with photographs of the light of the direct Sun, sufficiently enlarged by a microscope objective to reduce the intensity. Comparison of the intensities with photographs of the Moon taken on the voyage give a satisfactory accordance.

As the relative intensities as found on p. 111 are in satisfactory accordance with Turner's formula, he integrated according to this law from the Sun's limb to infinity, and found

$$3·2 \times 10^{-7} \text{ or } 16·3^m \text{ compared with the Sun,}$$
$$0·17 \text{ or } 1·9^m \qquad ,, \qquad ,, \qquad \text{Moon.}$$

Schwarzschild finds the Corona light compared with the Sun slightly weaker in the ultra-violet. In these observations he has allowed for the scattered light. These observations were the first made with a direct comparison with the Sun's light, and are a tribute to Schwarzschild's skill in photometry.

Graff used for the inner Corona a telescope of 20 metres focal length giving a diameter of the Sun 18·3 cm. or 7·3 inches, and for the outer Corona one of shorter focus. He used Schwarzschild's results to calibrate the scale of blackness, and finds for the total brightness 0·26 full Moon.

A photo-electric determination of the brightness of the Corona was made by Kunz and Stebbins[†] at the eclipse of 1918 under very favourable conditions. Their site was Rock Springs in Wyoming at an altitude of 6,500 feet, with the Sun at zenith distance 53·3°, and a totality of 95 seconds. The colour-sensibility of the potassium cell they used may be taken as 4,500 A. The cell was exposed directly to the Corona during totality and the galvanometer readings compared with those made on a standard electric lamp N before and after the eclipse. The intensity of this lamp was accurately determined in terms of a standard amyl-acetate candle. The deflexion of the galvanometer was found to be directly proportional to the intensity of the light. The cell was exposed to the light of the Corona and to the sky at a distance of 8° from the Sun. The programme of

[†] *Ap. J.* **49**, 137 (1919).

observations is summarized in the table extracted from the author's
paper.

| Time | Exposure to | Galvanometer reading | Deflexion | Unit = N at one metre | | | Corona in candle-metres |
				Corona +sky	Sky	Corona	
0	Dark	90 div.	0·0				
10	Corona	123	33·0	0·682	0·072	0·610	0·57
20	Sky	93	3·1				
30	Corona	125	35·1	0·723	0·072	0·651	0·61
40	Sky	93	3·1				
50	Corona	124	34·2	0·705	0·072	0·633	0·59
60	Dark	89·9	0·0				
70	Sky	92·8	3·1				
80	Corona	126	36·3	0·746	0·077	0·669	0·62
90	Sky	93·2	3·6				
100	Dark	89·5	0·0				

The mean result is 0·60 in candle-metres.

The observers obtained observations of the full Moon a fortnight
later after their return. The value was found to be 0·88 in candle-
metres with the Moon at a zenith distance of 65·3°. From stellar
photometric work they find an atmospheric absorption of 0·36^m for
the photometric cell on a clear night. Allowing for the zenith distance,
the Corona outside the atmosphere will have a brightness of 1·07
candle-metres and the full Moon 2·13 candle-metres, and the Corona
is 0·50 of the light of the full Moon.

Observations of a similar character were carried out by Briggs[†] at
Goodwindi in Australia at the eclipse of 1922. He obtained a value
of 0·22 candle-metres at mid-totality, but considerably larger values
0·34 and 0·27 near the beginning and end, which he attributes to the
brighter light of the inner Corona. If the mean value be taken, we
find 0·28. The Sun was at zenith distance 69°, so the values for
the brightness of the Corona outside the atmosphere are somewhat
uncertain, and are 0·62 candles or alternatively 0·79 candles.

Ross[‡] at the same eclipse, observed at Wallal in North Australia,
made a determination of the total light of the Corona by a direct
comparison with the full Moon a fortnight before the eclipse. A
suitable photometer was constructed by which the light of the
Corona was received on a photographic plate through a series of
circular apertures, a screen of finely ground glass being used to prevent
pin-hole images. By having three draw slides, two records of the

[†] *Ap. J.* **60**, 273 (1924).   [‡] *M.N.R.A.S.* **84**, 660 (1924).

light of the full Moon on September 6 and one of the Corona on September 21 were obtained on an Ilford Special Rapid plate. Also a record of the full Moon and Corona and a Hefner Amyl Acetate lamp on a Wellington anti-screen plate. The total light of the Corona compared with the Moon at the same altitude east of the meridian was 0·62 and west of the meridian 0·59 for the Ilford plate. For the anti-screen plate the coronal light was found to be 0·77 of the full Moon, whose light from the amyl-acetate lamp was determined as 0·18 lux. The anti-screen plate indicates that the light of the Corona is somewhat stronger in visual light.

Kunz and Stebbins[†] made another determination at the eclipse of 1925 near sun-spot minimum, using the apparatus they employed in 1918. They were unfortunate in having the Sun at the large zenith distance of 73°, but fortunate in having a break in the clouds at the time of the eclipse.

The light of the Corona was measured in candle-metres as 0·29. Assuming that the absorption at the zenith was $0·40^m$, they conclude that the total light of the Corona outside the Earth's atmosphere was 0·93, as against 1·07 in 1918. Thus for the three eclipses 1918, 1922, and 1925 the values of the brightness of the Corona in terms of the full Moon are 0·50, 0·37, and 0·43.

They conclude that no real difference has been established for a difference of the intensity of the Corona at sun-spot maxima and minima.

At the eclipse of 1925 Parkhurst[‡] determined the total light of the Corona by comparison with a Tungsten lamp of colour temperature 2,415° C. He observed the amount of transmitted light also through a green and blue filter. The Sun was at a low altitude 15·6°. He subtracted for the sky light by observing 8° east of the Sun. He compared the lamp with the Moon, but had to make a correction for phase and in some cases for altitude. His mean result is 0·27 times the full Moon. The reduction of the observations was nearly completed before his death, and the publication of the results was entrusted to Miss Farnsworth.

The total light of the Corona in blue and yellow light was determined by King[||] at the eclipse of 1925 January 24. Four photometers of 'pin-hole' type were used at Buffalo by Shapley, at Poughkeepsie by Miss Cannon, at New London by Leon Campbell, and at

[†] *Ap. J.*, **62**, 114, 1925.   [‡] *Ap. J.* **64**, 273 (1926).
[||] *H.C.O. Circular*, **286** (1925).

Nantucket by King. It was cloudy at Buffalo but clear at the other stations, where the Sun was at altitudes of 17°, 18°, and 20°. Exposures were of 4^s and 2^s over fields of 6° and 3° diameter respectively. By the use of neutral shades absorbing 1·9^m and 3·7^m for the blue and 1·8^m and 2·9^m for the yellow, carefully calibrated with the unshaded light, three gradations of intensity were furnished.

The plates were measured by a thermo-electric photometer and compared with a Hefner lamp. The results obtained at the three stations compared with the Hefner lamp and taken as of photographic magnitude −10·68^m and photo-visual −13·89^m are as follows:

Stellar Magnitude of Corona

	Photographic		Photo-visual	
	6°	3°	6°	3°
	m.	m.	m.	m.
Nantucket	−11·56	−11·06	−11·89	−11·60
New London . . .	−11·42	−11·12	−11·64	−11·78
Poughkeepsie . . .	−11·21	−10·71	−11·60	−11·44
	−11·40	−10·96	−11·71	−11·61

After elimination of the sky light, the photographic magnitude of the Corona is found to be −10·76^m and the photo-visual magnitude −11·57^m, giving a colour index corresponding to star of type G0. Taking Russell's value of photo-visual magnitude of the Moon as −12·55^m, the Corona is fainter by nearly one stellar magnitude, and its total light is 0·40 of the full Moon.

Bolometric Observations. The energy emitted from a small area of the Corona has been determined by the bolometer, and may be regarded as a measure of its 'surface brightness'. Then by integration according to a determined law of intensity the total brightness of the Corona may be found. Other observations, giving the distribution of this energy between different limits of wave-length, though more properly belonging to the spectral distribution, are given for convenience in this chapter.

Bolometric determinations of the intensities of the solar Corona were made by Abbot† at the eclipses of 1900 and 1908. At the eclipse of 1925 observations were made by Stetson and Coblentz‡ and by Pettit and Nicholson.‖

† *Ap. J.* **12**, 69 (1900); *Smithsonian Miscellaneous Collections*, **52**, part 1, 31 (1908).
‡ *Ap. J.* **62**, 128 (1925).   ‖ *Ap. J.* **62**, 202 (1925).

Abbot used a bolometer with a glass window fed by a mirror of 50·5 cm. diameter and focal length 100 cm., obtaining in this way a great concentration of light. He observed the transmission through a glass cell 3·00 cm. thick and also through a glass covered with asphaltum varnish which would cut out all the visible radiation. His conclusion was that the light of the Corona differs very little from that of the Sun. The intensity at a distance of 4′ from the Moon's limb he found to be $4·0 \times 10^{-7}$ compared with sunlight.

Stetson and Coblentz used a Newtonian reflector of 15 cm. aperture and 127 cm. focus. The thermopile was so arranged that the receiving surfaces of the thermocouple could be set simultaneously on the dark disk of the Moon, and then shifted so that one was 2′ outside the limb on the west and afterwards on the east. The size of each receiving surface was 1·5 mm. × 5 mm. A fluorite window transmitted all wave-lengths. By the interposition of a water cell (glycerine was actually substituted for water for fear of frost) most of the infra-red light is absorbed. Without the glycerine cell a deflexion of 1·35 cm. was obtained, and with the cell 0·4 cm. The authors conclude that a large percentage of coronal radiation comes from relatively low temperature emission.

Pettit and Nicholson used the 50·5-cm. mirror used by Abbot in 1908. It had been refigured so that the focal length was 101 cm. and gave an image of the Moon 9·79 mm. at the eclipse. A thermocouple and transmission cells were mounted in the focus of the mirror. The thermocouple had a rock-salt window which would transmit radiations of all wave-lengths. It had two junctions 0·76 mm. square separated by 5 mm. They were set alternately on two points, 4·6′ east of the limb and 12·4′ inside the disk, and 12·4′ inside and 4·6′ west of the limb. Two transmission cells were provided—a cell of saturated salt water 1 cm. thick and a cover-glass 0·165 mm. thick. Provision was made for the change of focus produced by the interposition of the water. The readings of a D'Arsonval galvanometer of high sensitivity were registered photographically. The results obtained were:

	Double deflexion
	mm.
Free	65·4
Water-cell . . .	47·1
Cover-glass . . .	61·4

The results were compared directly with sunlight by means of a small auxiliary mirror which was placed centrally over the 50·5-cm.

mirror, the large mirror being covered during the observations of the Sun. This spread the sunlight over a circle of 115 cm. in diameter at the thermocouple, reducing the intensity of the sunlight in the proportion $22 \cdot 07 \times 10^{-4}$. The deflexions obtained for the same altitude of the Sun were:

Deflexion

					mm.
Free	.	.	.	.	57·2
Water-cell	.	.	.	.	40·8
Cover-glass	.	.	.	.	56·2

The cover-glass transmits all wave-lengths from $0 \cdot 3\,\mu$ to $5 \cdot 5\,\mu$, while the water-cell only transmits light from $0 \cdot 3\,\mu$ to $1 \cdot 3\,\mu$. Allowing for a reflection of 7 per cent. from the cover-glass, there is no light from Sun or Corona of wave-length $> 5 \cdot 5\,\mu$. They find for the percentage distribution:

	$0 \cdot 3\,\mu$–$1 \cdot 3\,\mu$	$1 \cdot 3\,\mu$–$5 \cdot 5\,\mu$
Corona . .	77·6	22·4
Sun . . .	71·4	28·6

The Corona thus had slightly more light on the blue side of $1 \cdot 3\,\mu$ than the Sun.

Surface Brightness of the Corona. For the relative intensity at $4 \cdot 6'$ from the Moon's limb, the intensity of direct sunlight to that given by the large mirror is $41 \cdot 95 \times 10^{-5}$. This must be multiplied by $22 \cdot 07 \times 10^{-4}$, as the direct sunlight was weakened to this extent. Thus the radiation of the Corona compared with the Sun at $4 \cdot 6'$ from the Moon's limb is $9 \cdot 26 \times 10^{-7} \times 65 \cdot 4/114 \cdot 4$, or $5 \cdot 29 \times 10^{-7}$. A small correction applied to this makes the final ratio $5 \cdot 40 \times 10^{-7}$. This is in good agreement with a value of $4 \cdot 6 \times 10^{-7}$ obtained by Abbot from the 1908 eclipse at a distance of $4'$ from the Moon's limb. Using the value $5 \cdot 40 \times 10^{-7}$ the integrated intensity is found from the table on p. 113. $E = \dfrac{5 \cdot 40 \times \Sigma I A}{I_c}$, where I_c is the mean of the intensities at $4 \cdot 6'$ from the limb. In this way the total intensity of the coronal light in terms of the Sun is found to be $10 \cdot 1 \times 10^{-7}$ for the Seed 30 plates and $10 \cdot 7 \times 10^{-7}$ for the Ilford plates with the red filter.

Using Russell's value of the ratio of the visual light of the full Moon to that of the Sun, $21 \cdot 5 \times 10^{-7}$, the total brightness of the Corona is found to be $0 \cdot 47$ that of the full Moon.

Leaving the distribution of colour for later consideration, the

following list is believed to include most of the determinations of the
total light of the Corona:

Eclipse	Observer	Method	Full Moon
1886	Abney and Thorpe	Visual	0·8
1889	Leuschner	Visual	0·4
1893	Abney and Thorpe	Visual	1·1
1893	Turner	Photographic	0·6
1898	Turner	Photographic	1·1
1905	Fabry	Visual	0·75 or 0·55
1905	Knopf	Visual	0·85 or 0·62
1905	Schwarzschild	Photographic Spectrographic	0·17
1905	Graff	Photographic	0·26
1908	Abbot	Bolometric	0·40
1918	Kunz and Stebbins	Photo-electric	0·50
1922	Briggs	Photo-electric	0·33
1922	Ross	Photographic	0·60
1922	Ross	Visual	0·77
1925	Kunz and Stebbins	Photo-electric	0·43
1925	King	Photo-visual	0·40
1925	Parkhurst	Visual	0·27
1925	Pettit and Nicholson	Bolometric	0·47
1926	Stetson, Coblentz, Arnold, Spurr	Photo-visual	0·52

The total light may for the present be put down as 0·47 that of the
full Moon, which is near the mean of the most reliable determinations,
and is $1·00 \times 10^{-6}$ of the total light of the Sun.

POLARIZATION OF THE CORONA

Theory of Polarization of the Corona developed by Schuster.
Schuster† in 1879 pointed out very clearly the value of accurate
measurements of the polarization of light in the Sun's Corona. He
calculated the polarization due to the scattering of light by small
particles surrounding the Sun. We cannot do better than quote the
introductory paragraph of his paper.

'Before we can apply the theoretical results to the actual phenomenon,
we must take account of all the particles along a given line of sight. We
cannot do this, as we do not know the law of distribution of the scattering
particles round the luminous sphere. We are, therefore, obliged to discuss
various possible laws, and see how the theoretical results agree with the
observed facts. A further complication is introduced by a large and unknown quantity of unpolarized light mixed up with the Corona and most
likely due to incandescence. Our problem is an inverse one, and seems at
first sight very hopeless. From the observed polarization of light we are
to find out what part is due to scattering particles, and, as will be seen, we
cannot do this without finding out at the same time in what way the
scattering particles are distributed round the Sun and in what way the
light due to other causes varies with the distance from the Sun. I began
the calculation in the hope of getting a rough idea only of the amount of
polarization we might expect. But it appeared that even such observations as we can make during the short time available during a total eclipse
may yield most important information as to the constitution of the solar
Corona. I shall show that combined measurements of the polarization at
different distances from the Sun will be sufficient to determine all our
unknown quantities. We may hope to obtain, by means of the polariscope,
answers to the following questions:

'In what way is the scattering matter distributed in the solar atmosphere?

'What part of the light sent out by the Corona is due to scattering
matter?

'Is the scattering matter projected outward from the Sun, or is it falling
into the Sun from outside?'

According to Rayleigh's‡ formula, the light from an element of the
Sun's surface at M and scattered at P is resolved into two components:
B^2 polarized in the plane OPM, $B^2 \cos^2\alpha$ polarized in the plane at right

---

† *M.N.R.A.S.* **40**, 36 (1879).   ‡ *Phil. Mag.* **41**, 107 (1871).

angles to OPM, where α is the angle MPO. The intensity resolved in any plane forming an angle δ with OPM is

$$B^2(\cos^2\delta + \cos^2\alpha \sin^2\delta).$$

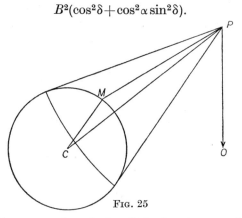

Fɪɢ. 25

By integration over the whole of the luminous sphere visible at P, Schuster finds for the light reflected by a volume element at P the amount polarized in the plane CPO is

$$g_0 = \frac{B^2}{3\pi}(1 - \cos\omega)(4 + \cos\omega + \cos^2\omega),$$

and the amount polarized in the perpendicular plane is

$$g_1 = g_0 - \frac{B^2}{\pi}\sin^2\chi(1 - \cos\omega)(\cos\omega + \cos^2\omega),$$

where ω is the angle between PC and the tangent to the sphere from P, and χ is the angle CPO.

Schuster went on to calculate the amount of polarization which would be found in the light reflected by a cloud of particles distributed according to various laws, the density being proportional to various inverse powers of the distance. The results are expressed as follows:

Let J be the total light received from any point in the Corona;

I_0 the amount of light from this point polarized radially;

I the amount of light polarized tangentially;

$2A$ the amount of light emitted which is not polarized at all.

Then $$J = I_0 + I + 2A.$$

The polarization in the radial direction is $I_0 - I$, and the fraction of the coronal light which is radially polarized is $P = (I_0 - I)/J$. The quantities $I_0 - I$ and I were originally calculated by Schuster† and recalculated in a form slightly better adapted for comparison with

† Loc. cit.

observation by Young. In both cases the calculations are given for densities proportional to r, r^{-2}, r^{-4}, and r^{-6}, while Young adds the case r^{-8}.

Young's Comparison of Schuster's Formulae with Observations. The only observation available to Schuster was that by Winter, at the eclipse of 1871 who determined the fraction of the polarization at 10′ from the limb as 26 per cent. From a general consideration of possible laws of density and their effect on the variation of $2A$ as the distance from the Sun is increased, Schuster concluded that the scattered light was not much more than half of the total light in the Corona of 1871.

A quantitative comparison of Schuster's formulae with observations is that made by R. K. Young,† who discussed the polarization photographs taken by Perrine at the eclipses of 1901, 1905, and 1908. In 1901 Perrine used a doubly refracting crystal placed in front of a telescope of 1-inch aperture and $21\frac{1}{2}$ inches focal length. In 1905 and 1908 he supplemented this by placing glass reflectors at the polarizing angle, with the planes of polarization perpendicular to each other in front of two telescopes of 3 inches aperture and 50 inches focal length. The photographs reproduced in the *Lick Observatory Bulletin* show to the eye a marked difference in the form of the Corona. The intensities were measured on a Hartmann microphotometer, the plates being placed on a rotating table. As no scale of intensities was made on the original plates, one was constructed on similar plates as far as possible in the same manner. In Fig. 26, taken from one of several in the *Lick Observatory Bulletin*, the plane and dotted lines give the curves of equal intensity, or isophotes, of the two photographs taken by the double-image camera. With Young's notation, a is the amplitude of vibration of unpolarized light, b is the amplitude of the vibration of the polarized light; k_1, k_2 are the measured intensities of the images parallel and perpendicular to the line in the plane normal to the reflecting polariscope. These normals were set as nearly as possible in the cardinal points. Then

$$b^2\cos^2\theta+\tfrac{1}{2}a^2 = k_1,$$
$$b^2\sin^2\theta+\tfrac{1}{2}a^2 = k_2,$$

and the percentage of polarization equals

$$\frac{b^2}{a^2+b^2} = \frac{k_2-k_1}{k_2+k_1}\bigg/(\cos^2\theta-\sin^2\theta).$$

† *L.O.B.* **205** (1911).

Owing to indeterminateness in the neighbourhood of 45°, measures were only used between +20° and −20° round each cardinal point.

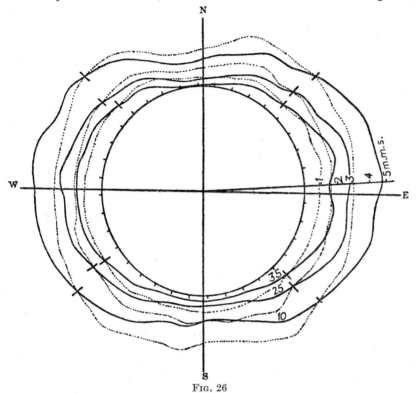

Fig. 26

The results from 3 plates in 1901, 4 in 1905, and 2 in 1908 are given below, and alongside is given the total intensity J obtained from photographs with the 40-foot telescope in 1905 and 1908.

Distance from Moon's limb	Percentage of polarized light = P	Relative intensity = J	PJ	PJ (corrected)
1′	18·0	5·42	0·976	0·85
2′	24·7	3·67	0·901	0·92
3′	33·2	2·44	0·810	0·83
4′	37·8	1·52	0·576	0·61
5′	37·4	1·00	0·374	0·41
6′	36·6	0·70	0·256	0·28
7′	37·0	0·51	0·188	0·19
8′	35·1	0·40	0·140	0·14
9′	35·8	0·30	0·109	0·11

The quantity P is the radial polarization, but it is possible by the use of Schuster's formulae to determine separately the amounts of radially polarized, tangentially polarized, and unpolarized light. The quantity PJ (corrected slightly to the distance from the Sun's, not the Moon's, limb) is equal to $I_0 - I$, and by comparison with Schuster's calculations it is possible to deduce a distribution law for the reflecting particles in the Corona; Young finds that the distribution of matter in the Corona is represented by $14r^{-6} - 8 \cdot 1r^{-8}$. He gives in the following table the observed and calculated values of $I_0 - I$ on this assumed value of the density:

Distance	(Calculated)	(Observed)	O.—C.
1′	·0·95	0·85	−0·10
2′	0·85	0·92	+0·07
3′	0·70	0·83	+0·13
4′	0·57	0·61	+0·04
5′	0·44	0·41	−0·03
6′	0·34	0·28	−0·06
7′	0·28	0·19	−0·09
8′	0·22	0·14	−0·08
9′	0·18	0·11	−0·07

He is then able to calculate I_0 and I separately, and finds $2A$ the unpolarized part.

Distance	$I_0 + I_1$	J	2A (percentage)
1′	4·55	5·85	22
2′	3·06	3·98	23
3′	1·81	2·69	33
4′	1·29	1·68	23
5′	0·92	1·08	15

His conclusions are:

1. The polarization of the light in the Corona is radial.
2. The percentage of polarized light increases rapidly from the limb, reaching a maximum of 37 per cent. at a distance of 5′, and then falls slowly to 35 per cent. at a distance of 9′.
3. The Corona is formed by matter projected from the Sun.
4. Two-thirds or even a greater percentage of the light emitted by the Corona is due to the scattering of small particles.

The only criticism we have to make of Young's paper is his assumption for the law of density. If the assumed law had been the sum of an inverse 6th and 8th power there would have been no objection. But a difference of two powers seems somewhat artificial.

Using the inverse 6th power, we find:

Distance	I_0-I_1	I_0+I_1	J	$2A$ (percentage)
1'	1·01	4·67	5·85	20
2'	0·83	2·93	3·98	26
3'	0·64	1·86	2·69	31
4'	0·49	1·25	1·68	26
5'	0·37	0·89	1·08	18
6'	0·28	0·62	0·71	13
7'	0·21	0·45	0·54	17
8'	0·17	0·31	0·41	24
9'	0·13	0·21	0·30	30

The agreement of I_0-I with the observations is not so good, but the results are in general agreement with those obtained by Young.

Observations by Dufay and Grouiller, 1932. At the eclipse of 1932 Dufay and Grouiller[†] placed a doubly refracting prism of Iceland spar before the slit of their spectroscope, and thus obtained spectra of light polarized in two perpendicular directions.

Comparison of the two spectra showed that the polarization was independent of the wave-length and that it reached a maximum of 26 per cent. at a distance of 10' from the limb.

Visual Observations by Johnson, 1934. Visual observations of polarization are made with difficulty during the short time of an eclipse, but they have been made from time to time, and they indicate that about one-third of the coronal light is unpolarized.

At the eclipse of 1934 Johnson[‡] used a diffraction polarimeter designed by Lyot which made it possible to measure the fraction of polarized light to one part in a thousand. Measuring from the east limb, he finds the following percentages at the distances indicated, which may be compared with Young's figures:

Distance from limb	Percentage of polarization, P.	
	Visual (Johnson)	Photographic (Young)
1·0'	17	18
1·9'	23	24
4·1'	26	38
6·5'	25	37
8·5'	28	35

Atmospheric Polarization. A difficulty with the determination of polarization in the Corona arises from the possible polarization

† C.R. **196**, 1574 (1933).   ‡ P.A.S.P. **46**, 226 (1934).

due to the Earth's atmosphere. Observers have sometimes found
no atmospheric polarization, but others have found polarization,
usually in a vertical direction. We shall confine ourselves to the
observations of Newall[†] and Salet,[‡] who observed the eclipse of 1905
from stations in Tunis about 30 miles apart. Newall found from
visual observations made with a Savart polariscope that polarization
was approximately vertical or horizontal. In this instrument a plate

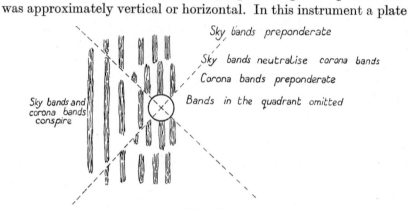

Fig. 27

of quartz is cut at an angle of 45° with the optic axis, and in
association with a Nicol prism the instrument gives a series of inter-
ference bands when the incident light is polarized. If the light is
polarized at right angles to the plane of transmittance, a dark central
band is obtained, accompanied on both sides by parallel coloured
fringes. If the incident light is polarized parallel to the direction
which can pass through the analyser, the central band is bright and
the whole effect is complementary to that found in the previous case.
Newall also obtained a photograph at the same eclipse with a similar
instrument and obtained a result shown in Fig. 27.

The vertical atmospheric bands in the upper and lower quadrants
are out of step with those in the left-hand and right-hand quadrants.
The coronal polarization is therefore radial and the atmospheric
polarization horizontal. At a distance of $\frac{3}{4}$° from the centre of the
Corona the intensity of the coronal polarization is equal to that of
the atmospheric polarization.

Salet carried out similar observations at the same eclipse. He
looked for evidence of a magnetic field in the Corona in the shape of
small deviations of the plane of polarization from the radial, and

† *M.N.R.A.S.* **66**, 475 (1906).   ‡ *C.R.* **141**, 528 (1905).

found a deviation of 2·5° by visual observation. This deviation was confirmed by photographs taken during the eclipse. Salet found that the plane of polarization of atmospheric light was vertical—a result exactly the opposite of Newall's, although the two eclipse camps were only 30 miles apart. Salet found that the polarization of the Corona was a maximum at 5′ or 6′ from the limb of the Sun, and that it could be traced outwards for one or one and a half solar diameters. The fact that both Newall and Salet were able to detect polarization at distances of 25′ or so from the limb, where the intensity of the coronal light has diminished to a hundredth part of its intensity near the limb, is of importance, and seems to indicate a very high degree of polarization.

Recent Observations. Dufay and Grouiller† confirmed their results (p. 131) at the eclipse of 1936 August 31 and found that polarization of the Corona reached a flat maximum of 26 per cent. at a distance of 10′ from the limb and is independent of wave-length over the range 4,000 A.–5,700 A. They conclude that the continuous spectrum of the Corona is due to the scattering of sunlight by free electrons.

Cohn,‡ on the contrary, finds from the eclipse of 1934 Feb. 14 differences in the amount of polarization for the light of different wave-lengths from 4,200 A. to 6,680 A. The polarization in the red reaches 57 per cent. at 6′ from the limb. He concludes that the scattering is not due solely to free electrons.

† *C.R.* **203,** 453 (1936).
‡ *Nature*, 1937 Jan. 2, p. 29. A preliminary account of the method of observation is given in *P.A.S.P.* **46,** 177 (1934).

THE SPECTRUM OF THE CORONA

THE spectrum of the Corona was first observed as a continuous band in 1868 by Rayet. In 1869 Harkness and Young discovered a bright line in the green. In 1871 Janssen found absorption lines, including the D line of sodium, in the continuous spectrum. Schuster in 1886 concluded that the continuous spectrum had its maximum farther in the red than the maximum of the solar spectrum. This was confirmed by Deslandres in 1893, but was definitely contradicted by Schwarzschild in 1905. The fact that the colour of the spectrum is identical with that of the Sun was established by Ludendorff from observations of the eclipse of 1923, and was confirmed by Grotrian in 1926. The existence of dark lines has been attributed to sunlight scattered by the Earth's atmosphere. But their presence has been placed beyond doubt by Moore, Ludendorff, and Grotrian. Additional bright lines were discovered by Lockyer in 1893 and by later astronomers.

Absorption Lines. Polariscopic observations indicate unmistakably that a large part of the coronal light is reflected sunlight. The presence of dark lines in the spectrum of the Corona was found by Janssen in 1871. The possibility that these arose from the sunlight scattered by the Earth's atmosphere threw some doubt on this result. In 1883 Janssen assured himself that the dark lines were coronal. Photographs, notably those taken by Perrine in 1901, showed dark lines, but there was still some doubt whether these had not arisen from scattered sunlight. Moore,† at the eclipse of 1922 September 21 in Australia, with a small dispersion and a long exposure, obtained the spectrum of the Corona to a distance of 35′ from the Sun. Fraunhofer lines were found, particularly in the violet, but no trace of lines was found beyond the limits of the Corona spectrum. The coronal lines were stated to be broader and fainter than the corresponding solar lines. By comparison with an iron spectrum inside the dark disk of the Moon, displacements to the red of 26 km. were found both on the east and west of the Corona at a distance of 20′ from the Sun's limb. As this light is, in the main, at any rate, reflected sunlight, an outward movement of the particles of the

† *P.A.S.P.* **35**, 333 (1923).

Corona of 20 to 30 km./sec. is indicated. This was verified, but not so satisfactorily, in 1932.

Ludendorff† at the eclipse of 1923 September 10 found no Fraunhofer lines within 5′ of the Sun's limb, but beyond this limit they were seen weaker (*flauer*) but not broader than the corresponding lines in the solar spectrum. No reproductions of Moore's or Ludendorff's spectra have been given as far as we are aware, probably on account of the difficulty of publishing satisfactory positives. Ludendorff's spectrum was put under a Zeiss microphotometer by Grotrian.‡ The

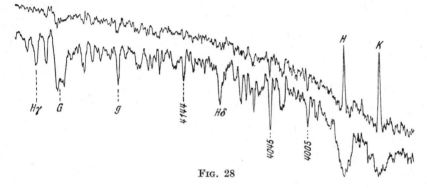

Fig. 28

trace at a distance of 14′ from the limb is given with the solar spectrum for comparison.

The strong absorption lines at 4,005 A., 4,045 A., 4,144 A. and the *g* line occur in the Corona spectrum with practically the same width as in the solar spectrum, confirming Ludendorff's conclusion.

Continuous Spectrum. Many attempts have been made to determine the distribution with wave-length of the intensity of the continuous spectrum of the Corona, the first measurement being made by Schuster‖ at the eclipse of 1886 August 29. He found that 'the maximum of actinic intensity of the coronal light was decidedly more towards the red end of the spectrum than that of Sun light'. Deslandres§ found a similar result in 1893. During both these investigations the Corona was veiled for at least a part of the exposure by cloud. Another important investigation was conducted by Schwarzschild†† at the eclipse of 1905 August 30. He found that in the range

† *Sitzungsberichte der Preus. Akad. der Wiss.* **5**, 83 (1925).
‡ *Zs. f. Astrophys.* **8**, 124 (1900).
‖ Darwin, Schuster, and Maunder, *Phil. Trans.* **180**, 326 (1890).
§ *Annales du Bureau des Longitudes,* **5**, 40 (1897).
†† *Astron. Mitteilungen der Kgl. Sternwarte zu Göttingen,* **13**, 18 and 59 (1906).

3,500–5,000 A. the intensity distribution of the Corona spectrum agreed in general with that of the solar spectrum, but that when the differences were analysed, it was seen that the intensity maximum of the Corona was shifted slightly towards the red as compared with sunlight.

It was left to Ludendorff,† and following him Grotrian, definitively to establish the fact that the intensity distribution of the coronal spectrum coincides with that of the normal solar spectrum at least within a limit of $0 \cdot 1^m$. This was done by very careful photographic photometry which may serve as a model to all spectrophotometric observers.

It will be remembered that photographic photometry is carried out as follows. Let D be the density of a photographic image, measured by any photometer. This density D may be described numerically by the deflexion of an electrometer needle or by the setting of a wedge on another sort of photometer, but it is essentially dependent on the size of the silver grains and the number deposited in 1 sq. mm. of the photographic image. Then let I_λ be the intensity of the light which gave rise to this image. There will be in general some relation between photographic density and light intensity, or

$$D = f(I_\lambda),$$

where the form of f is dependent on the time of exposure, the circumstances of development, and the wave-length λ. It is in general unknown, and each plate has to be calibrated in each wave-length that is used. We have in addition Schwarzschild's relation

$$D = f(I_\lambda t^p),$$

relating the densities of images made with different exposure times t. Here p is an index which is again dependent on the exact circumstances of the development and must be determined for each plate as it is used. Since general relations between D, I, λ, and t cannot be used, it is necessary in determining intensity as a function of wave-length to conduct the observations in such a way as to form a comparison of the object under examination with a body whose colour-intensity function is known, e.g. a black body. It is at once desirable to eliminate the coefficient p (which is difficult to determine with accuracy) by giving equal exposure times on object and comparison (Corona and black body). Further, it is desirable to use the relation $D = f(I_\lambda)$ as little as possible, by making the densities of object and comparison as nearly equal as possible. If it is not possible

† Loc. cit.

to use a black body which has approximately the same colour distribution as the object, it is desirable to reduce the colour differences
by interposing suitable colour screens. In the case of the Corona,
however, there is available for comparison a body whose colour
distribution is known, namely the Sun itself; and since it is known
that the Corona and Sun have at any rate roughly the same colour
distribution, the intensity distribution of the Corona with wave-
length is best determined by comparison with the Sun itself. The
use of the Sun rather than a terrestrial black body eliminates the
necessity for determining atmospheric extinction coefficients. Now
the Sun is very much brighter than the Corona—a matter of 15
magnitudes—so that equal exposure times can only be given to
Corona and Sun-comparison if some means of reducing the intensity
of the latter is employed.

Ludendorff compared the intensity distribution of the Corona
with that of the Sun by a method based on the above considerations.
The exposure times on Corona and comparison were made equal, and
the sunlight was reduced in intensity by interposing in the optical
system a plane surface of chalk, from which a diffuse reflection was
taken, and a number of coarse wire gratings, which were inserted
alternatively, so that a number of comparison spectra of differing
densities were secured. He obtained in this way at least one comparison spectrum a little denser than and one a little lighter than
the coronal spectrum, and the use of the relation $D = f(I_\lambda)$ was
restricted to interpolation over a small range in very wave-length
measured. The results require a small correction for the variation
in the reflecting power of chalk with wave-length. Corona and comparison were exposed on different days, the Sun's zenith distance
being the same. Ludendorff worked between 3,820 A. and 4,840 A.
He found that between these limits the intensity–wave-length curve
of the Corona coincides with that of the Sun within the limits of
observation, and that the observed differences nowhere exceed a
tenth of a magnitude. In particular, the intensity maximum of the
Corona spectrum has the same wave-length as that of the solar
spectrum. The intensity distribution is the same at all heights above
the Sun's limb in the Corona.

Ludendorff's results were confirmed and extended by Grotrian†
at the eclipse of 1929 May 9. Three spectrographs were mounted on

† *Zs. f. Astrophys.* **2**, 106; **8**, 124.

a single polar axis, the optical parts of one being made of quartz, so that the coronal spectrum from 3,400 A. to 6,500 A. was obtained. In addition to Ludendorff's chalk reflector and wire grating, Grotrian employed a step wedge over the slit of each spectrograph.

On each of the three spectrographs exposures of 52 seconds and $3\frac{1}{2}$ minutes respectively were made during totality (on May 9). The comparison spectra, made on the Sun itself when at the same zenith distance as at the time of the eclipse, were obtained on May 13 and May 15, using both 52 seconds and $3\frac{1}{2}$ minutes as exposure times. These were made on plates which were either cut from the same plate or taken from the same packet as the eclipse plates. All pairs were developed together on May 20 and May 21. Each comparison plate has a number of spectra of different intensity, and it is possible in every case to find two solar spectra such that one, S_a, is just stronger and one, S_b, just weaker than the coronal spectrum K in every wave-length.

The difference in magnitudes of the intensities of S_a and S_b is Δm_{ab}, being the difference in magnitudes between the transmissions of two steps on the step filter, and is determined by laboratory experiment. The spectra S_a, K, and S_b were passed through a registering photometer; tracings are reproduced in Fig. 28, p. 135. Let the deflexion of the electrometer needle at a given wave-length on the coronal spectrum be α_K, and let the deflexions on the comparison spectra at the same wave-length be α_{Sa} and α_{Sb}. Then the magnitude difference between the coronal spectrum K and the solar spectrum S_a is

$$\delta = (\alpha_{Sa} - \alpha_K) \frac{\Delta m_{ab}}{\alpha_{Sa} - \alpha_{Sb}}.$$

In stating this relation it is assumed that the density-intensity relation in between the curves S_a and S_b is a straight line, which is legitimate if the magnitude difference Δm_{ab} is small. The question under investigation is whether δ is a function of the wave-length or not. A correction to δ has to be applied for the deviation from constancy of the reflecting power of chalk.

This method of colour photometry is ideal, as the measurements actually made are measurements of small differences of density between Corona and comparison spectrum, the exposure times being equal. Grotrian finds that throughout the range 6,500–3,400 A. the values of δ never exceed $0\cdot1^m$. In making this comparison he found that the colour curve of the coronal spectrum follows the solar colour curve when a smoothed value of the latter is taken over the region 4,000 A.–3,700 A., where there is a great concentration of Fraunhofer absorption: thus the coronal spectrum shows Fraunhofer absorption smoothed out by some process so that the individual lines are unrecognizable. Grotrian emphasizes the fact that his work is essentially an extension of Ludendorff's as to the range of wave-length dealt with, together with the improvement of the step filter.

Other measurements of the colour intensity distribution of the continuous spectrum of the Corona have been made by Davidson, Minnaert, Ornstein, and Stratton† at the eclipse of 1926, and by Pannekoek and Doorn‡ at that of 1927. In neither case was the accuracy of the photometry at all comparable with that of Luden-dorff and of Grotrian, and both reductions make use of the Schwarz-schild coefficient. Photographic photometry was not introduced into the programme of the 1926 expedition until a late date, and no time was available for the design of adequate calibration apparatus. The observers had to content themselves with photographing the solar spectrum with successive exposure times of 1 sec., 2 sec., and 4 sec. by way of providing calibration marks. (It is at once necessary to assume a value for the Schwarzschild coefficient to find the density-intensity relation from such marks.) Davidson obtained an exposure of $2\frac{1}{2}$ minutes on the Corona with a quartz spectrograph: a high prominence overlaid the Corona during half of the exposure. The coronal continuous spectrum is shown from 4,150 A. (the edge of the plate) towards shorter wave-lengths. The well-exposed spectrum extends to H and K, and then dies away suddenly so that it has practically disappeared at 3,900 A. When this spectrum was put through the microphotometer the colour temperature of the Corona between wave-lengths 4,100 A. and 3,850 A. was found to be 2,000°.

The great weight of Grotrian and Ludendorff's work must be held to prove that the colour temperature of the Corona is the same as that of the Sun itself. It is true that Grotrian finds a dip amounting to 0·3^m between 4,100 A. and 3,850 A., precisely the region used in the 1926 result into which the effect of the dip might enter as the Corona follows the integrated effect of the Fraunhofer lines, and presumably the comparison spectrum was picked out in between the Fraunhofer lines. But the difference in gradients between the

† *M.N.R.A.S.* **88**, 536 (1928).   ‡ *Verh. K. Akad. Amsterdam*, **14**, 21 (1930).

black-body curves for 2,000° and 6,000° is such that there is a magnitude difference of 0·8ᵐ at 3,850 A. if the spectra are matched at 4,100 A. This means that the photographic photometry in the 1926 result is responsible for an error amounting to half a magnitude. The density at 3,850 A. on Davidson's film is near the threshold value, and the exposure on the Corona was 270 sec., compared with 1 sec. to 4 sec. on the comparison solar spectra, so that a great burden was thrown on the Schwarzschild coefficient.

The continuous spectrum of the Corona was photographed by N. W. Doorn at the eclipse of 1927 June 29. Two exposures were made, from 5ˢ to 8ˢ and from 11ˢ to 27ˢ after totality. The continuous spectrum of the Corona is well exposed. Photometric calibration of the plates was performed by imprinting the spectrum of a lamp emitting like a black body at 2,662° through a step wedge, the exposure times on these comparisons being 9ˢ, 90ˢ, and 900ˢ. The spectrum from 6,030 A. to 4,900 A. was received on a panchromatic plate abutting an ordinary plate, which received the spectrum from 4,900 A. to 3,900 A. The two plates exhibit slightly different curves when the intensity of the Corona is plotted against distance from the limb, though the curves have the same shape for different wavelengths on the same plate. This points to some photometric error. Pannekoek and Doorn discussing the results consider that 'a difference of spectral distribution (between Corona and Sun) cannot be derived with certainty from the results, because the relative values for larger and smaller wave-lengths depend to a high degree on the different Schwarzschild coefficients p adopted for the two plates'. Over the range 6,030–4,400 A. the magnitude differences between Corona and Sun do not exceed 0·2ᵐ on either plate. Both plates show a high value at 4,000 A. and a low value at 3,900 A., the mean of the two plates at 3,900 A. being 0·6ᵐ lower than the average from 6,030 A. to 4,400 A. The results obtained by Pannekoek and Doorn involve the adopted atmospheric transmission coefficients.

Pannekoek and Doorn conclude their memoir dealing with the results of the eclipse expedition by remarking that it is necessary to make the comparison spectra with as nearly as possible the same exposure time as the eclipse plates. This means that in practice it is desirable to dispense with the Schwarzschild relation $D = f(I_\lambda t^p)$ and work solely with the relation $D = f(I_\lambda)$, which can only be done by giving equal, or nearly equal, exposure times to eclipse and comparison plates—a principle which will be generally admitted by all workers who have experience of photographic photometry in the present decade.

To this must be added the information obtained from the bolometric observations given in Chapter XIII. Abbot concluded that the distribution of light from the Corona differs little from that in the Sun. Stetson and Coblentz, on the contrary, found a much greater radiation from the infra-red. Their apparatus was so much smaller than the large concentrating mirror used by Abbot and later by Pettit and Nicholson that the latter results are to be preferred. These give 77·6 per cent. of the coronal light between 3,000 A. and 13,000 A., as against 71·4 per cent. from the Sun. The bright Corona lines which give perhaps 1 per cent. of the total coronal light will explain part of the difference. The conclusion that the coronal light is essentially the same as sunlight, apart from the bright lines, is not set aside by the bolometric measurements.

Bright Lines in the Spectrum of the Corona. In 1869 Harkness found a bright line in the green in the continuous spectrum of the Corona. Young identified the line he found in the green with the iron line numbered 1474 on Kirchhoff's scale. The difficulty of the identification of lines by visual observation under eclipse conditions must excuse subsequent observers for not having corrected this mistake for thirty years. In 1898 Lockyer's[†] expedition to India obtained photographs of the spectrum of the Corona with a prismatic camera. A number of distinct rings were shown and on measurement the green ring was found to have the wave-length 5,303·7 A. instead of 5,316·8 A., corresponding to K 1474. Rings were found corresponding to wave-lengths 3,800, 3,987, 4,231, 4,359, 4,568, and 5,303 A. A spectroscopic camera has this advantage over a slit spectrograph that it shows the distribution of each radiation round the Sun's limb, which often exhibits condensations in a few places. Comparison of the rings showed a similarity of those at 4,085, 4,231, and 4,588 A. with that at 5,303 A. The rings at 3,800 A. and 4,568 A. were similar to that at 3,987 A. These similarities suggested the possibility that the radiations might proceed from the same element.

At the same eclipse slit spectroscopes were used by Campbell, Newall, and Hills. The slit spectroscope has the advantage of giving more accurate values of the wave-lengths. With this object, Campbell

† *Phil. Trans.*, Series A, **197**, 151 (1901).

and Moore† at the eclipse of 1918, with a light flint prism of 60°, determined the wave-lengths and intensities and lengths of the coronal lines from 3,601 A. to 5,303 A. With a spectrographic camera they obtained the distribution of the intensity of 5,303 A. round the Sun's limb, and in a drawing show that the condensations occur in the neighbourhood of prominences. They also give an historical account of coronal observations, and include a table of measures of wave-length from those of Fowler and Deslandres in 1893 up to 1918. Their complete list includes a number which they recognize as doubtful. In addition to several faint lines discovered since 1898, attention may be drawn to the strong line at 3,601 A. found by Lewis and by Campbell and Albrecht in 1908, and the red line at 6,374 A. found by Carrasco and by Bosler and Bloch in 1914. As an illustration of the great intensity of the 5,303 A. line in the neighbourhood of a prominence, the spectrum obtained by Dyson in 1905 is reproduced in Plate 10. The slit was placed nearly tangential to the Sun's limb at the point of second contact, and an exposure of about $2^m 45^s$ given from 15^s after the commencement of totality to 15^s from the end. The advancing Moon cut off the exposure from the centre of the line. The chromospheric lines in the lower part of the spectrum arise from a large prominence which happened to be near the point of second contact.

At the eclipse of 1918 the expedition from the Lowell Observatory obtained a slit spectrum of the Corona with two single-prism spectrographs and one with three prisms and one without slit. In spite of thin haze these were very successful in showing the distribution of the continuous spectrum and the great extension of the line at 5,303 A.

The attempts by Campbell and Moore to obtain accurate wave-lengths of the lines at 5,303 A. and 6,374 A. by the use of a grating failed owing to the faintness of the lines in 1922 and to clouds in 1923.

At the eclipse of 1926 Davidson and Stratton‡ obtained with a quartz spectrograph accurate wave-lengths of the lines from 3,388 A. to 4,086 A. and with a flint spectrograph from 6,374 A. to 5,303 A. By a comparison of the variation of intensity of the lines at different distances from the limb they confirm the results of Lockyer's 1898 expedition in the similarity of 3,454, 3,643, and 3,601, 4,086 A.; and also add the pair of lines at 3,388 and 3,987 A. With a spectrographic

† *L.O.B.* **318**; *Phil. Trans.*, Series A, **206**, 403 (1906).
‡ *Mem. R.A.S.* **64**, 105.

PLATE 10

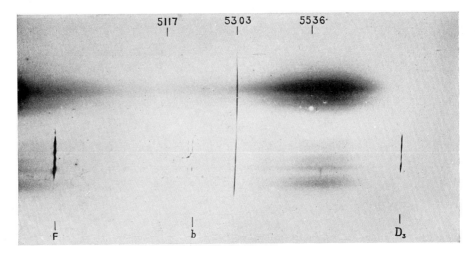

SPECTRUM OF CORONA. 1905

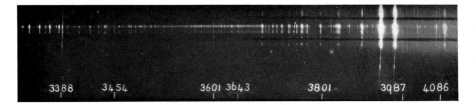

ULTRA-VIOLET SPECTRUM OF CORONA. 1926

camera they also obtained the rings of 6,374 A. and 5,303 A. The ring at 5,303 A. shows condensations in three places in the neighbourhood of prominences. Davidson and Stratton made a critical examination of the lines previously found by observers and rejected a number of doubtful lines and some others which appeared to be chromospheric rather than coronal.

At the eclipse of 1930 Mitchell† ventured to take two very fine concave gratings to a volcanic island in the South Pacific and was rewarded by very fine photographs of the coronal rings. The diameter of the Sun was 14·5 mm. and the dispersion 10·9 A. per millimetre. Mitchell published drawings of the rings 6,374 A. and 5,303 A. and more detailed drawings of the condensations on the east and west limbs. Both of these are in the neighbourhood of prominences. He points out that the intensities are very provisional and may vary from eclipse to eclipse.

Grotrian at the eclipse of 1929 added two new lines at 3,328 A. and 6,374 A.

Intensities of the Emission Lines of the Corona. At the same eclipse Grotrian‡ made a careful investigation of the intensities of the emission lines. He took three spectroscopes with which he covered the whole range of spectrum from 6,700 A. to 3,200 A. The slits were placed nearly tangential to the Sun at the point of second contact. He had the good fortune to have a prominence near this point. Exposures of $3\frac{1}{2}$ minutes and 52 seconds were given. By placing the slit in this position he had a greater length of spectrum for each interval of 1' in distance from the Sun's limb.

With a Hartmann photometer the total blackening of each line and continuous spectrum was compared with that of the continuous spectrum in the immediate neighbourhood. The diagram from Grotrian's paper (Fig. 29) shows the intensity in stellar magnitudes of combined line and continuous spectrum and of the continuous spectrum alone at varying distances from the limb, the difference of the ordinates giving the excess in magnitudes of the line above the continuous spectrum.

From these curves and ten others not reproduced here it is seen that there is in general a parallelism between the upper and lower parts of the diagram, indicating that the intensity of the bright lines falls off proportionately to that of the continuous spectrum. There

† *Ap. J.* **75**, 1 (1932).   ‡ *Zs. f. Astrophys.* **2**, 106; **7**, 26.

are, however, some differences, such as the increase of intensity in
5,303 A. at 2′ from the limb. Grotrian uses these differences to place
the lines in groups and compares the results with those of Lockyer and
Fowler, Campbell and Moore, Davidson and Stratton, and Mitchell.
The conclusion with which Mitchell and the authors agree is that the

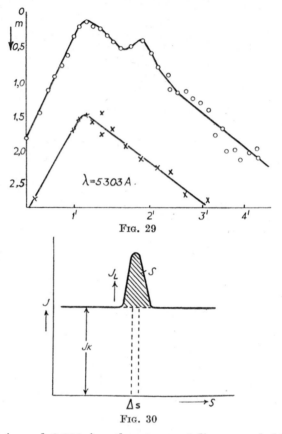

FIG. 29

FIG. 30

lines 5,303 A. and 3,888 A.—the strongest lines—probably have a
common origin, but no clear case is made out for any other lines.

   For the actual intensities of the Corona lines a Zeiss registering
photometer was employed, and at a distance of 2·5′ from the limb,
an area of 0·2 mm. in length and 0·005 mm. in breadth was measured.
Fig. 30 sufficiently illustrates the method. Let $J = J_k + J_l$, where
J is the total intensities measured by the microphotometer, and
J_k is the intensity of the continuous spectrum and J_l of the emission
line in the neighbourhood.

Further, let $S = J_l\,ds$, where S is the coordinate measured by the microphotometer.

Let $\Delta s = S/J_k$.

Then the equivalent breadth of the line $\Delta\lambda$ is given by

$$\Delta\lambda = \Delta s \frac{d\lambda}{ds}.$$

As the distribution of the intensity in the Corona spectrum agrees with that in the solar spectrum, $\Delta\lambda$ is multiplied by $F(\lambda)$, which is the energy distribution of the solar spectrum in arbitrary units. In this way the following table is obtained.

Intensities of Coronal Lines measured by Grotrian

λ	$\Delta\lambda$, in Angstroms	$F(\lambda)$	$F(\lambda)\Delta\lambda$	Intensity		Previous estimate
				$5{,}303 = 100$	$3{,}388 = 20$	
3328	0·7	3·6	2·6	1·0	1·2	8
3388	11·1	4·0	44·4	16·4	20·0	20
3454	1·4	4·7	6·4	2·3	2·9	8
3601	1·1	5·5	5·8	2·1	2·6	12
3987	0·2	7·8	1·8	0·7	0·8	5
4087	0·3	8·4	2·6	1·0	1·2	6
4231	0·8	9·2	7·0	2·6	3·2	8
4567	0·3	10·5	3·1	1·1	1·4	3
5118	1·2	10·3	11·8	4·3	5·3	3
5303	27·5	9·9	272	100	122	20
6374	2·8	7·9	22·1	8·1	10·0	6
6704	2·0	7·4	14·8	5·4	6·7	4

The intensity of 5,303 A. is much greater than 3,388 A. apart from its multiplication by $F(\lambda)$.

Grotrian remarks that the bright lines contribute not more than 1/180th part of the total energy of the Corona, and that the green line contributes not more than 1/100th part of the visible light, and has no perceptible effect on the colour of the Corona.

Spectrum of Corona obtained without an Eclipse. In a previous chapter a description has been given of Lyot's method of observing the Corona without an eclipse. This observer successfully applied his instrument to the distribution of coronal lines round the limb, and accurate determinations of their wave-lengths and intensities were obtained. A full description of the spectrograph and spectroheliograph employed with his coronagraph is given in the *Zeitschrift für Astrophysik* (**5**, 73 (1932)). Using a concave Rowland grating of

U

14·5 cm. and radius 7 m. in the second order and correcting the astigmatism with a cylindrical lens, Lyot obtains a dispersion of 1·2 A. per millimetre. The images are somewhat faint and require a long exposure. Using instead of the grating a 61° flint prism traversed twice, he has a dispersion of 5 A. per mm. in the green, but the smaller dispersion is compensated by the exposure time being 15 times as rapid as that required by the grating spectrograph. The spectro-heliogram taken in the light of the green ray is shown in the central part of Plate 11. The exterior part shows the green ray in different parts of the disk with exposures of 10 minutes. It may be noted that the ray is strongest in the neighbourhood of a spot.

As a result of these researches Lyot finds that the width of the green ray is 1·2 A. and is of regular form as seen under a micro-photometer. In parts of the Corona near the limb the line attains an equivalent breadth of 70 milliangstroms of the continuous solar spec-trum. The wave-length was determined from the 1931 observations to be 5302·85 A., and the difference of the East and West measures gave a rotation value a little less than that of the Sun, but subject to great uncertainty. The red ray is given a wave-length of 6,374·75 ±0·15 A. Radiations at wave-lengths 4,232, 4,086, and 3,986 A. were not found.

Lyot's[†] observations were continued in 1934 at the Research Institute on the Jungfraujoch, a station at an altitude of 3,450 metres. He found that the green ray which had been feeble in high latitudes in the year 1931 and very strong within 30° of the Equator was in 1934 strong in high latitudes, and sometimes invisible at the Equator. The red line at 6,374 A. was more uniformly distributed in both years.

Observations of the green ray were made on seven days between August 10 and August 24, and of the red ray on four days from August 16 to August 24. Measures of the intensity were made at 55″ from the limb. From the diagrams for the distribution of the intensity on these days those for August 10 and August 24 are reproduced in Fig. 31. On August 24 the green ray was visible to heights of 3′ 55″, 4′ 25″, and 3′ 10″ in the three quadrants NW., WS., and SE. From August 10 to August 24 the Sun had turned through 185°. It is seen that the principal jets of the Corona accompanied the Sun in its rotation.

† *C.R.* **200**, 219 (1935).

PLATE 11

SPECTROHELIOGRAM OF THE CORONA IN THE LIGHT OF 5,303 A. (*Lyot*)

Lyot's observations† were continued at the Pic du Midi in August and September 1935. The green ray 5,303 A. was strongly seen, but 5,118 and 5,536 were not seen. 6,374 was strongly seen, and 6,702, found by Grotrian at the eclipse of 1929, is clearly shown. Nothing was found between 6,800 A. and 7,600 A. The spectrum was examined as far as 10,300 A. in the infra-red and a new line of intensity equal to that of 6,374 was found at 7,892 A.

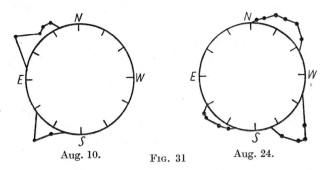

Aug. 10.   Fig. 31   Aug. 24.

Lyot has determined the true contours of the coronal lines by comparison with monochromatic solar lines in the neighbourhood. He finds for the three first lines contours which approximate closely to the radial velocities of the molecules of a gas. Their equivalent breadths are

$$0{\cdot}80 \text{ A. for } 5{,}303 \text{ A.}$$
$$0{\cdot}97 \quad ,, \quad 6{,}374$$
$$1{\cdot}07 \quad ,, \quad 6{,}702$$

It should, however, be noted that if the breadths of the lines are due to thermal velocities, the atom must have a mass much smaller than that of hydrogen.

M. Lyot has kindly forwarded to us the following results obtained at the Pic du Midi in the spring of 1936. He used a plane Rowland grating of 4 inches and a camera lens of focal length 1 metre. For the rays of 10,746 A. and 10,797 A. the first order was used with a dispersion of 15 A. per mm., the third order (5·3 A. per mm.) for the line 3,388 A., the second order (7·5 A. per mm.) for the other lines. The intensities at a distance of 35″ from the Sun's limb are compared with the intensity of 1 A. of the continuous solar spectrum. The line 3,388 A. was measured at a distance of 60″

† *C.R.* **202**, No. 14 (April 6, 1936).

from the limb, and its intensity is not comparable with the other intensities.

Wave-length	Exposure	No. of plates	Intensity
	h. m.		
3,388·10±0·07	0 35	2	..
5,116·03±0·03	0 18	3	$2·6 \times 10^{-6}$
5,302·86±0·03	0 18	4	120×10^{-6}
6,374·51±0·03	0 27	4	28×10^{-6}
6,701·83±0·03	0 33	4	$3·3 \times 10^{-6}$
7,059·62±0·05	0 40	2	4×10^{-6}
7,891·94±0·07	1 0	3	29×10^{-6}
8,024·21±0·10	1 0	1	$1·3 \times 10^{-6}$
10,746·80±0·10	4 10	1	240×10^{-6}
10,797·95±0·10	4 10	1	150×10^{-6}

The wave-lengths given are the means of the East and West limbs. The rotation of the Corona has been measured on two plates for the green line, giving 0·086 A. and 0·064 A. for the differences East minus West.

As the coronal radiations change from one part of the limb to another and as different radiations generally show little relationship with one another, the intensities of the lines are definitely variable. Lyot finds that they also vary from day to day and consequently exact values cannot be given. It is surprising that the estimates made by different observers at different eclipses show so good an accordance in their relative strengths. Taking Grotrian's measures of the intensity of the emission lines in terms of 1 A. of the continuous spectrum of the Corona, and taking the total light of the Corona to be 10^{-6} that of the Sun, and on the assumption that its intensity falls off as the inverse 6th power of the distance from the centre, then in the neighbourhood of the limb the intensity is 4×10^{-6} of the intensity of sunlight. In this way we obtain a rough comparison of Grotrian's with Lyot's intensity for three lines.

	Lyot	Grotrian
5,303 A.	120×10^{-6}	110×10^{-6}
6,374 A.	28	11·2
6,706 A.	3·3	8

The following list of the Corona lines contains all, as far as we know, that have been found to the present time. The measures made by Grotrian have been converted into the same units as those by Lyot, namely, $10^{-6} \times 1$ A. of the solar spectrum at the corresponding wavelength. The intensities in the last column are the results of estimates at many eclipses. Where a probable error is attached the wavelength has been taken from Lyot.

Wave-length	Int. $10^{-6} \times 1A.$ Grotrian, 1929	Int. (esti-mated)	Wave-length	Int. $10^{-6} \times 1A.$ Lyot, 1936	Grotrian, 1929	Int. (esti-mated)
3,328	2·8	8	4,567	..	1·2	3
3,388·10±0·07	44·4	20	4,586	..	..	2
3,454·1	5·6	8	5,116·03±0·03	2·6	4·8	3
3,601·0	4·4	12	5,302·86±0·03	120	110	20
3,642·9	..	3	5,536	..	..	2
3,800·8	..	3	6,374·51±0·03	28	11·2	6
3,986·9	0·8	5	6,701·83±0·03	3·3	8·0	4
4,086·3	1·2	6	7,059·62±0·05	4	..	..
4,231·4	3·2	8	7,891·94±0·07	29	..	6
4,311	..	2	8,024·21±0·10	1·3	..	..
4,359	..	4	10,746·80±0·10	240	..	..
			10,797·95±0·10	150	..	..

Coronal Lines in RS Ophiuchi. No coronal lines have as yet been identified in any terrestrial spectra, nor till recently in the spectra of any star. In 1933 Adams and Joy[†] found the lines 3,987 A., 4,086 A., 4,231 A., and 6,374 A. in the spectrum of RS Ophiuchi. This star suddenly increased its brightness from 11·0[m] to 4·3[m] and like T Pyxidis is subject to repeated outbursts. In 1898 it reached a brightness of 7·7[m] and was designated Nova Ophiuchi No. 3 by Pickering, with a spectrum classification Oc. In 1923 Adams, Humason, and Joy obtained its spectrum when of magnitude 11·5 and classified it as G 5. Observations at Mount Wilson in August 1933 showed changes in the spectrum of the star similar to those found in Novae, bright nebular lines being shown on August 31. On September 2 the He[+] line 4,686 A. showed a strong band. The green line 5,303 A. was seen on October 2, though it appears to have been observed by Müller[‡] as early as September 3. The structure of the lines is similar to the He[+] line 4,686 A., having a sharp violet component and a faint red component. In May 1934 the coronal lines had disappeared and the spectrum was similar to that of 1923.

The similarity of the coronal lines in this star to the lines of ionized helium suggests that this element is a possible origin of the lines. Helium lines are known to be greatly strengthened in the higher chromosphere, and recently H. D. and H. W. Babcock[||] have found the coronal line 5,303 A. associated with He lines in the higher chromosphere. According to Goudsmit and Wu,[††] it is not likely that the coronal lines will be identified as forbidden lines in any spectrum

† *P.A.S.P.* **45**, 249, 301 (1933); **46**, 223 (1934).   ‡ *A.N.* 5975, 5984, 5986.
|| *P.A.S.P.* **46**, 132 (1934).   †† *Ap. J.* **80**, 154 (1934).

on the same basis as the well-known nebular forbidden lines, on account of the great width of the coronal lines; Wright and Curtis[†] have failed to obtain interference patterns of coronal radiation, and Lyot[‡] finds equivalent breadths of order 1 A.; great natural width in a line goes with a short lifetime of the excited state of the atom which emits the line, and the nebular forbidden lines are emitted by atoms in metastable states which possess long lives—of order 1 sec. as opposed to the usual 10^{-8} sec. found in ordinary excited states. It was originally suggested by Rosenthal[||] that the coronal lines form part of a spectrum of helium in which both electrons are in excited states (the normal spectrum being emitted when one electron remains always in the unexcited state). This suggestion is repeated by Goudsmit and Wu, who give approximate energy levels for the doubly excited He atom. It is not possible to compute accurate wave-lengths, but it appears that such a spectrum would at least show some lines in the visible spectrum. There are, however, two difficulties to be faced: firstly, why do not the coronal lines fit into a Rydberg series if they belong to a single spectrum, and, secondly, if the coronal lines are due to doubly excited He atoms, why are the ordinary He lines absent in the Corona? These objections are answered by Beutler,[††] who contends that the absence of a Rydberg series is explained by perturbations which arise in doubly excited He, since many series with equal symmetry properties converge to neighbouring limits, and that the absence of the He and He[+] lines from the Corona spectrum is accounted for by the fact that the lines 5,303 A., etc., are excited by fluorescence following on the absorption $(1s)^2 \to 3d(mp)$ at about 170 A., while the absorptions $(1s)^2 \to 2s(mp)$ and $(1s)^2 \to 2p(ml)$ at about 190 A. are rare since the spectral regions which would excite the last mentioned excitations are absorbed in the lower layers of the solar atmosphere by the continuous absorption of the He[+] and O[++] spectra, which have their limit at 225 A.

This theory of the origin of the coronal lines cannot, unfortunately, be allowed to pass without criticism. According to Goudsmit and Wu, the states of doubly excited He from which these coronal lines originate have an excitation potential of no less than 60 volts, requiring radiation of wave-length so short as 170 A. for their excitation. Now suppose that the Sun radiates like a black body at

† *J. Opt. Soc. Amer.* **21**, 154 (1931).   ‡ *C.R.* **202**, 391 (1936).
|| *Zs. f. Astrophys.* **1**, 115 (1930).   †† *Zs. f. Astrophys.* **9**, 387 (1934).

6,000° K., then if all the solar energy emitted in wave-lengths below 200 A. were concentrated in the coronal lines by a fluorescent process, these lines would exhibit a total luminosity of 10^{-44} of the Sun's luminosity or 10^{-38} of the luminosity of the Corona. They are observed to contribute about one-half of 1 per cent. of the luminosity of the Corona according to Grotrian; the great discrepancy between these figures suggests that the lines must originate in states with a much lower excitation potential. We have otherwise to suppose that the solar radiation traversing the Corona is extraordinarily rich in radiation of wave-length about 170 A.

THE NATURE OF THE CORONA

Early Theories of the Nature of the Corona. A good deal of speculation and research has been given to the nature of the Sun's Corona. One of the earliest attempts was made by Schaberle† in 1890 from the two eclipses in the previous year. He constructed a 'Mechanical Theory' of the Corona based on the principle that the streamers consisted of matter ejected from the Sun, and moving in elliptical streams about the Sun's centre as focus. These streams came from the sun-spot zones and fell back into the Sun unless they were projected with velocities greater than 600 km. per second. Schaberle constructed a model of a typical Corona. Objection was raised that an annual change in the form of the Corona should occur owing to the perspective effect due to the position of the Earth in relation to the Sun's Equator. Photographs of the eclipse of 1893 were given a most careful scrutiny by Schaberle, and although the theory that the forces involved are mainly gravitational must be rejected, the view that the coronal streamers are shot out with eruptive prominences seems tenable. As a very rough picture, we may think of the jets issuing from a rotating garden hose.

Sabine's discovery in 1852 of a relation between terrestrial magnetic phenomena and the sun-spot cycle appeared at the time to indicate the existence of magnetic forces in the Sun, and the connexion between solar magnetism and the Corona is strongly suggested by the appearance of the Corona near sun-spot minimum, which is suggestive of lines of force surrounding a magnetized sphere. Bigelow‡ compared the Corona of 1889 with the lines of force due to a magnetic doublet at the Sun's centre and coaxial with the Sun's axis of rotation, and found some correspondence between the two. The existence of strong magnetic fields associated with sun-spots was demonstrated by Hale in 1908, and the same observer together with his colleagues at Mount Wilson gave with much uncertainty, the general magnetic field of the Sun as having a strength of 50 gauss in the reversing layer and falling off in intensity farther out. Störmer‖ put forward in 1911 a dynamical theory of the Corona based on the

† *Contributions of the Lick Observatory*, No. 4.
‡ *Smithsonian Institute*, No. 691 (1889).
‖ *C.R.*, **152**, 425 (1911).

assumption that it consists of electrons emitted from the Sun passing through a weak magnetic field. The electrodynamics of coronal streamers has also been discussed by Rosseland.†

In 1905 Schwarzschild pointed out that there was no 'Rayleigh blue' in the Corona and suggested that the coronal light was sunlight scattered by electrons. The rapid thermal velocities of the electrons imply an absence of Fraunhofer lines in the coronal light; thus, as Rosseland‡ points out, at a temperature of 4,000° K. an electron has a thermal velocity of 216 km./sec. which would broaden a line to a half-width of 10 A. at 5,000 A. At much lower temperatures than this the Fraunhofer lines would be completely obliterated. Although the presence of Fraunhofer lines in the Corona was first reported by Janssen, this fact had not certainly been established in Schwarz-schild's day, and its confirmation beyond the possibility of doubt was only made by Moore and Ludendorff much later. The Fraun-hofer lines would naturally be supposed to arise from the reflection of photospheric light by particles in the Corona having a mass considerably greater than the electron. The thermal agitation of the lightest atom, hydrogen, at 4,000° K. would not broaden the lines by more than about 0·2 A., while other atoms would of course broaden them less. That part of the coronal spectrum which exhibits Fraun-hofer lines might be attributed to the reflection of sunlight by a cloud of atoms or ions were it not for the difficulty that it is known that the light of the Corona is white, whereas sunlight reflected by bodies of atomic dimensions should exhibit the Rayleigh blue; and it might be attributed to the reflection of sunlight by dust particles were it not for the fact that a solid body distant one radius from the photosphere would be raised to a temperature of 3,000°, at which it would presumably volatilize rapidly. Before describing attempts to escape from the dilemma presented by these considerations of the nature of the Corona, we here recapitulate the experimentally deter-mined facts.

1. The intensity of the continuous spectra of the Corona falls off very rapidly from the solar limbs.

2. Within 5' of the limb the Corona spectrum is purely a continu-ous spectrum. Outside this limit the Fraunhofer lines appear, weaker than in the solar spectrum but of the same width as in the solar spectrum.

† *Publ. Oslo Univ. Obs.*, No. 5.   ‡ Ibid., No. 1.

3. The light of the continuous spectrum is partly polarized. The polarization is a maximum at a distance of about 10′ from the limb.

4. Emission lines appear in the inner Corona and extend to at least 5′ from the limb. See Fig. 29, p. 144.

5. The Fraunhofer lines in the Corona exhibit a red-shift relative to the solar lines, which indicates an outward velocity of the scattering particles of the order of 20 km./sec. at a distance of 10′ to 20′ from the limb.

The Corona considered as composed of Particles of Atomic Dimensions. The view that the scattering particles in the Corona responsible for the Fraunhofer spectrum are atoms or ions has been discussed by Minnaert† in a paper 'On the Continuous Spectrum of the Corona and its Polarization' in which he makes a new reduction of Young's polarization observations. The primary difficulty in the path of an explanation along these lines is the white colour of the Corona. Particles of atomic dimensions should exhibit a scattering coefficient proportional to λ^{-4}, i.e. they should show the Rayleigh blue. The light scattered by such atoms is polarized, and since according to Young's observations some of the coronal light is unpolarized, it is possible to assume that the Corona emits a radiation of its own: it might for example emit a black-body radiation corresponding to some temperature less than that of the photosphere, say about 3,000°. Minnaert's theory is that the light emitted by the Corona is red in colour and that the sum of this reddish light and the blue light consequent upon the Rayleigh scattering by the atoms in the Corona gives the observed white light of the Corona.

On this hypothesis the Corona spectrum can be considered as the sum of three parts: (a) a white continuous spectrum, polarized, due to reflection by electrons; (b) a blue polarized spectrum due to reflection by ions or atoms showing the Fraunhofer lines; and (c) the proper emission of the Corona, reddish and unpolarized. The degree of polarization should be expected to increase from red to blue. Minnaert points out that visual observations show only 11 per cent. of polarization, while photographic observations show 35 per cent., the figures on their face value fitting in with a λ^{-4} law for the polarized light. In claiming this result he has to suppose that the spectrum (a) is negligible, but it is not likely that great weight can

† *Zs. f. Astrophys.* **1**, 209 (1930).

be attached to the visual observations. It is in any case difficult to account for emitted light of sufficient intensity to balance that from reflection.

After the publication of Minnaert's paper Dufay and Grouiller[†] at later eclipses measured the polarization of the Corona in various wave-lengths. Their observations showed conclusively that the polarization is independent of the wave-length over the spectral region which they studied (from 3,889 A. to 5,876 A.). Dufay and Grouiller remark that 'the Corona, whose spectral energy curve is practically identical with that of the Sun, and which is polarized in almost the same proportion in all wave-lengths, diffuses light like a gas of free electrons', but this view ignores the fact that the Corona shows the Fraunhofer lines.

Minnaert noted of his own theory that it was not possible to reconcile the strength of the spectra (*b*) and (*c*) relative to (*a*) required by the theory with theoretical physics. He remarks: 'In the observations themselves there is nothing against the assumption that the scattered light of the Corona is due to ions or atoms. There is only the theoretical argument against it, which, however, is very strong.' One must now add that the observations of Dufay and Grouiller demolish Minnaert's theory in its original form, and as far as they go leave no alternative to Grotrian's dust theory—which has its own difficulties. One may perhaps say of the Corona, considered as an assembly of atoms and electrons ejected from the photosphere, that the most singular feature is the complete absence of any emission lines such as those of H and Ca^+ which are so conspicuous in the chromosphere and prominences.

The Corona Particles considered as Dust Particles. Grotrian carefully analysed the problem in a paper 'Über das Fraunhofersche Spektrum der Sonnenkorona',[‡] and came to the conclusion that the Corona spectrum which exhibits the Fraunhofer lines is reflected by particles having a diameter of at least three times the longest wavelength at which the colour of the Corona is observed to agree with that of the solar disk, making the diameter of the particles at least $3\,\mu$. The paper describes the results of spectrophotometric measurements of the Fraunhofer lines in the Corona spectrum. Grotrian divides the Corona spectrum into two parts: (1) the continuous spectrum arising from the reflection of photospheric light by electrons,

[†] *C.R.* **196**, 1574 (1933).   [‡] *Zs. f. Astrophys.* **8**, 124 (1934).

and (2) the Fraunhofer spectrum arising from the reflection of photo-spheric light by dust particles.

Let J_S be the intensity of the spectrum at some point in the Corona, J_K the intensity of the continuous spectrum (1), J_F the intensity of the Fraunhofer spectrum (2). Further, let J_R, $J_{R'}$ be the central intensities of a particular absorption line in the normal solar spectrum and in the total spectrum of the Corona. Measurement of the central

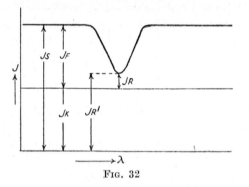

Fig. 32

intensities in the Sun and Corona gives respectively the quantities $J_R/J_F = C_S$, say, and $J_{R'}/(J_K+J_F) = C_K$, say. But $J_{R'} = J_K+J_R$, from which we deduce that

$$J_K/J_F = (C_K-C_S)/(1-C_K).$$

For the G line, for example, Grotrian finds $C_S = 0.46$, while C_K varies from 0.08 to 0.31 as the distance from the limb increases from 5.6' to 26.4'. Grotrian's results obtained from G, g, 4,144 A. and 4,045 A., are given in the following table.

Grotrian's Analysis of the Continuous Spectrum of the Corona

East limb				West limb			
h	J_S	J_F	J_K	h	J_S	J_F	J_K
′				′			
..	..	..	..	1.2	272	..	..
..	..	..	..	2.3	150	..	..
3.2	97.4	15.8	81.6	3.5	99.5	12.4	87.1
5.6	46.3	8.8	37.5	5.8	39.2	7.5	31.7
7.9	23.2	5.4	17.8	8.1	17.6	4.8	12.6
10.2	12.6	3.7	8.9	10.4	9.7	3.4	6.3
12.5	7.6	2.5	5.1	12.7	5.8	2.5	3.3
14.8	4.6	1.8	2.8	14.4	3.8	1.85	1.95
19.5	1.9	1.0	0.9	19.7	1.3	0.9	0.4
24.1	0.9	0.6	0.3	..	..	..	..
26.4	0.63	0.48	0.15	..	..	..	..

In the last table it may be noted that the Fraunhofer spectrum is more symmetrically distributed than the continuous spectrum.

Grotrian attributes the continuous polarized spectrum to electron scattering, and he attributes the Fraunhofer spectrum to scattering or reflection by particles of dimensions at least 3μ: this spectrum is supposed by him to be unpolarized. On this theory the Sun is surrounded by a symmetrically distributed cloud of dust particles which at greater distances from the Sun are responsible for the zodiacal light. Grotrian points out that the falling off in intensity of the zodiacal light is consistent with the very reasonable law that the intensity varies as $(\operatorname{cosec} e)^{\frac{3}{2}}$, where e is the angular distance as seen from the Earth. Changes in the form of the Corona and want of symmetry in the Corona are attributed to changes in the electron streams issuing from the photosphere and giving rise to the continuous spectrum. The chief difficulty attached to this theory is the high temperature which a dust particle would attain in the neighbourhood of the Sun, which would cause it to volatilize. This has been pointed out by Anderson[†] and Russell,[‡] the latter giving a formula $4{,}050° \, (R/r)^{\frac{1}{2}}$ for the temperature of a conducting black sphere at a distance r from the centre, R being the radius of the Sun.

It is not necessary to suppose that Grotrian's dust cloud extends right up to the photosphere: what appears to be the inner Corona consists of particles which are almost in the line of sight with the limb. Even so Moore's observations of the expansion of the dust cloud are a further difficulty: dust particles might be falling into the Sun from cooler regions and resisting volatilization for some time, but if the material is issuing from the Sun or even being blown outwards by radiation pressure (as Grotrian suggests), it is obvious that the radius at which solid particles will be found will be farther out than the limit at which inward falling particles continue to exist.

On Grotrian's theory the quantity J_F/J_K is identical with the ratio of unpolarized to polarized light, or $2A/(J_t+J_r)$ in Young's analysis. Grotrian finds J_F/J_K equal to 0·23 at 5′ from the limb and 0·47 at 10′ from the limb, while Minnaert, rediscussing Young's results, finds 0·35 and 0·50 for $2A/(J_t+J_r)$ at these distances from the limb, the corresponding quantity p being 0·36.

Dufay and Grouiller found 0·26 for p in 1932, and it appears likely, according to Grotrian, that the values of p alter from eclipse to eclipse.

† *Zs. f. Phys.* **28**, 299 (1924).   ‡ *Ap. J.* **69**, 49 (1929).

There is a general agreement as to order of magnitude between Grotrian's J_F/J_K, which refers to the eclipse of 1923, and values of $2A/(J_t+J_r)$ determined at other eclipses.

Two experimental tests of Grotrian's theory remain to be performed, the comparison of J_F/J_K and $2A/(J_t+J_r)$ at one and the same eclipse, and the observation whether the Fraunhofer spectrum of the Corona is indeed identical with the unpolarized light of the Corona, as Grotrian supposes it to be. Even if the results of these two experiments, which it may be hoped will be performed at an early eclipse, are favourable to the dust theory of the Corona, it will still have to face the difficulty of volatilization at the relevant temperatures. The nature of the Corona seems accordingly destined to remain one of the outstanding puzzles of astrophysics during the next decade.

INDEX OF NAMES

Abbott, 122, 123.
Abney, 117.
Adams, J. C., 37.
Adams, W. S., 68, 82, 149.
Airy, 38, 52.
Albrecht, 142.
Anderson, 157.
Andrews, 116.
Arago, 52.
Arnold, 57.
Aston, 71.

Babcock, 149.
Baily, 37, 51, 52.
Barabascheff, 33.
Barkowski, 53.
Barnard, 56, 105.
Baxendall, 67, 73.
Becker, 112.
Bellamy, 45.
Bergstrand, 107, 108, 112.
Berry, 30.
Bessel, 14.
Beutler, 150.
Bigelow, 152.
Blaserna, 54.
Bloch, 142.
Bohr, 70.
Bolansky, 113.
Bosler, 142.
Briggs, 120.
Brigham, 34.
Brown, 37.
Burns, 71.
Burwell, 68.
Butler, 103.

Campbell, Leon, 121.
Campbell, W. W., 44, 48, 61, 66, 71, 72, 141, 142.
Cannon, 121.
Carrasco, 142.
Carroll, 63.
Chandrasekhar, 97, 98, 101.
Chant, 50.
Chauvenet, 23.
Clerke, 51.
Coblentz, 57, 122, 123, 141.
Comrie, 23.

Conder, 32.
Cottingham, 44.
Cowell, 39.
Crommelin, 44.
Curtis, 71, 150.
Curtiss, 44.

Damoiseau, 37.
Danjon, 31.
D'Arturo, 104.
Davidson, 44–50, 70, 74, 75, 104, 139, 142.
Delaunay, 37.
De la Rue, 53.
Deslandres, 108, 134, 135, 142.
Dodwell, 50.
Doorn, 79, 80, 139, 140.
Dreyer, 29.
Dufay, 32, 131, 155.
Dunham, 73.
Dunthorne, 36.
Dyson, 66, 68, 104, 142.

Eddington, 44, 94, 96.
Einstein, 43.
Evershed, 65, 66, 67.

Fabry, 118.
Farnsworth, 121.
Fesenkov, 31.
Fotheringham, 24, 39.
Fowler, 64–70, 142.
Freundlich, 43, 48.
Frost, 66.

Ginzel, 9, 38.
Goudsmit, 149, 150.
Graff, 118, 119.
Grotrian, 134–9, 143–5, 148, 155–7.
Grouiller, 131, 155.

Hale, 68, 108, 152.
Halley, 36.
Hansen, 9.
Hansky, 104, 105.
Harkness, 54, 111, 134, 141.
Harwood, 113.
Hills, 66.
Hipparchus, 29.
Humphreys, 67.

Iniguez, 69.

Jackson, 27, 49, 105.
Janssen, 53, 54, 55, 134, 153.
Jeffreys, 41.
Jenvall, 114.
Johnson, 131.
Joy, 149.

Keenan, 32.
King, 113, 121.
Klüber, 114.
Knopf, 118.
Kunz, 119, 121.

Langley, 54, 55.
Laplace, 36, 37.
Leuschner, 117.
Lewis, 142.
Lippmann, 61.
Lockyer, Norman, 53–5, 64–73, 134, 141.
Lockyer, W. J., 64, 105.
Lord, 66, 67.
Ludendorff, 105, 107, 134–9, 153.
Lundmark, 112.
Lyot, 108–10, 145–9, 150.

McCrea, 99–101.
Marriott, 104.
Maunder, 104.
Melotte, 47.
Menzel, 71–4, 78–87.
Miller, 60, 104.
Milne, 89–98.
Minnaert, 75, 78, 83–8, 92, 101, 139, 154–7.
Mitchell, 66–74, 80–9, 92–101, 107, 108, 143, 144.
Moore, C., 82.
Moore, J. H., 34, 134, 142, 153, 157.
Müller, 149.

Newall, 66, 69, 132, 141.
Newcomb, 38.
Newton, H. W., 80.
Nicholson, 35, 112, 122, 123, 141.

Oppolzer, 9.
Ornstein, 75, 139.

Pannekoek, 78–88, 92, 101, 139, 140.
Parkhurst, 121.
Pauli, 76.
Perepelkin, 80, 113.
Perrine, 104, 134.
Pettit, 35, 112, 122, 141.
Plana, 37.
Plaskett, H. H., 98.
Pogson, 53.
Prazmowski, 53.

Ramsay, 53.
Ranyard, 56, 105.
Rayet, 53, 134.
Respighi, 54.
Rosenthal, 150.
Ross, 120.
Rosseland, 101, 153.
Russell, 35, 80, 82, 157.

Sadler, 25.
Saha, 70.
Salet, 132.
Schaberle, 60, 103, 152.
Schoch, 10, 40.
Schram, 10.
Schrödinger, 76.
Schuster, 55, 126–8, 135.
Schwarzschild, 75, 111, 118, 134, 135, 152.
Secchi, 53.
Semegken, 33.
Shackleton, 64.
Shapley, 121.
Slocum, 104.
Spencer Jones, 47.
Spurr, 57.
Stebbins, 119, 121.
Stetson, 57, 116, 122, 123, 141.
Stone, 54.
Störmer, 152.
Stratton, 70, 74, 75, 78, 104, 139, 142.

Struve, 52.

Taylor, 40.
Tennant, 53.
Thorpe, 117.
Trumpler, 48–50.
Turner, 62, 111, 117.

Unsöld, 99, 100.

Waley Cohen, 71.
Wesley, 103, 104, 105.
Whipple, 53.
Willard Fisher, 34.
Williams, 80–9, 92–101, 104.
Winter, 128.
Woolley, 80.
Wright, 150.
Wu, 149, 150.

Young, C. A., 54, 64.
Young, R. K., 50, 112, 128–31.

PRINTED IN GREAT BRITAIN AT THE UNIVERSITY PRESS, OXFORD
BY JOHN JOHNSON, PRINTER TO THE UNIVERSITY